Sip by Sip

Candid Conversations With People Diagnosed as Adults with Fetal Alcohol Spectrum Disorder (FASD).

Patricia Kasper

Table of Contents

Advance Praise
For
Sip by Sip: Candid Conversations with People Diagnosed as Adults with Fetal Alcohol Spectrum Disorders (FASD)

"What an incredibly insightful book that speaks from the hearts of a special population of individuals who have been diagnosed as adults with Fetal Alcohol Spectrum Disorders (FASD).

"They speak of their incredible frustrations with the public around them who lack any awareness of FASD as well as the medical profession which lacks not only awareness, but also a basic knowledge about this disorder; they speak about the stigma they have had to endure, the impairments in memory they have lived with; the anxiety they have experienced and the accommodations they have had to acquire to make life a little smoother. And they speak about the fulfilment and gratification they have felt from working with the FASD Changemakers as well as the stress and struggles they and their parents have had to cope with leading to their FASD diagnosis followed by the feeling of relief a diagnosis has given them.

"Patti Kasper has put together an outstanding book. She has been able to bring her own unique point of view to an extraordinarily complex subject in a way from which we can all benefit and learn."

- **Kenneth Lyons Jones, MD**
Distinguished Emeritus Professor
Department of Pediatrics University of California, San Diego La Jolla, CA

"This book is a moving and fascinating glimpse into the experience of having fetal alcohol spectrum disorders, a welcome perspective after the usual ones of how to manage one's children's disruptive behaviors! There is still a lot to be learned about what traits and quirks really are common to all of us and which occur rarely, but there is a thread running through all of these stories. It has to do with one quality of FASD that does seem to be universal, and that is the appearance of normalcy. Which leads to

profound misunderstanding by the rest of the world and even oneself. This compendium really illuminates what has long remained a dark and murky corner in the lives of a lot of us."

– Kathryn Page, Ph.D.

"In this illuminating book, Patricia gives voice to adults living with Fetal Alcohol Spectrum Disorder through a series of candid conversations. Each interview provides an intimate window into the many lived-experiences and perspectives of people with FASD. This collection of conversations validates and gives hope to all those whose lives have been shaped by FASD."

**-   Nate Sheets,
Author of Essential FASD Supports**

"Sip By Sip" is a deep dive into the world of FASD (Fetal Alcohol Spectrum Disorder) through the narrative of adults, living with a FASD....the MOST important voices of the FASD community! As a mom of a young adult with an FASD, I know that it often takes families years to receive the appropriate and proper FASD diagnoses for their children. In this compelling book, the author carefully crafts her conversations with adults, who are living with FASD. The most common theme among them is NOT being heard, the lack of knowledge of FASD amongst medical and educational professionals, and not being diagnosed until later in life - and this gives the reader insight into why it's SO important to be educated about FASD and to advocate for the 1 in 20 individuals living with this invisible disability!

**- Natalie Vecchione
Mom of Two, FASD Parent Advocate,
Co-Founder and Host of FASD Hope Podcast,
Co-Author of "Blazing New Homeschool Trails: Educating and
Launching Teens with Developmental Disabilities"**

Sip by Sip is an invaluable resource for individuals and families on the FASD journey! Patti creatively weaves her own story and the stories of other people living with FASD together to create not only an enjoyable read but a fact-filled book. The book is packed full of FASD facts, symptoms and personal experiences. It's a must read for parents, caregivers, and anyone with or working with someone with an FASD.

- **Sandra Flach**
Executive Director
Justice for Orphans, Inc.

This book is dedicated to my husband, Alan, for his patience and grace throughout this project, and support of my dream, and to my mother, Anna, who has always encouraged me on my path of lifelong learning. It is also dedicated to all those who have struggled throughout their lives with feeling different or less than or broken, never realizing their struggles had a biological basis. May this book provide hope as well as a path for you to explore.

Acknowledgments

I am grateful to Colleen Nordgren, who steered me towards deepening my understanding of FASD when I was working as a post-adoption social worker. I am indebted to Colleen also for her generosity and creativity in creating the cover art for Sip by Sip. I want to thank Natalie Vecchione and Robbie Seale, whose FASD-related podcasts have blessed me and countless others whose lives are touched by FASD. I am beyond grateful to a dear friend, who asked to remain anonymous, for her constructive feedback and helping me to hone this book to its present state. She managed to balance out her affection and support of my passion with reading through the manuscript with a critical eye. Because FASD interferes with my prowess in editing, she functioned as my external brain in this task, and for this, I am eternally grateful! Last but not least, I am grateful to Nathalie Brassard and the other facilitators at FASCETS (Fetal Alcohol Spectrum Consultation Education & Training Services), who changed my life, professionally and personally, through their program.

Thank you to all who previewed my manuscript. I very much appreciate the time you took out of your busy schedules to read, reflect and then provide your feedback and encouragement!

Lastly, but far from least, I wish to express my heartfelt gratitude toward each of my contributors: Rebecca Tillou, Gina Schumaker, CJ Lutke, Emily Hargrove, Jessica Birch, Nury van Beers, Kathryn Page and Debbie and Bill Michaud.

Without you, there would be no book. Each of you generously shared of your time and of yourselves. I cannot begin to thank you for your willingness to be vulnerable by sharing within these pages. I am blessed to be able to consider each of you as friends now that we have met. I thank you for standing up to the stigma with me, so that others who need answers may find them.

About the Author

Patricia Kasper, MA, MTh, has served for three decades in the fields of addictions, mental health and child welfare. With three Master Degrees (Master of Arts in Professional Psychology, Master of Theology in Messianic Studies, Master of Theology in Rabbinic Studies), she has provided faith based counseling as well as served as a congregational, praise and worship leader. She became an entrepreneur as a trainer and coach to make a greater stand for neurodivergence due to a variety of factors, most passionately due to prenatal exposure to alcohol. She is an authorized TBRI Practitioner, a Certified Facilitator of FASCETS Neurobehavioral Model and a Certified Virtual Coach. She also has the experience of living with FASD. Her company, Patricia Kasper, MA, MTh, Training Services, LLC provides staff development training and coaching services, serving not only parents of children with brain-based differences but neurodivergent adults as well. Patti is married and caring for her mother, who has dementia. Patti has a YouTube channel @Patricia Kasper Your FASD Coach, and has recently started a podcast, Living with FASD.

Prologue
FASD: a Growing Epidemic

Fetal Alcohol Syndrome (FAS) was discovered in 1973 by Dr. Kenneth Lyons Jones and Dr. David L. Smith, pediatricians at the University of Washington who were studying congenital abnormalities that arise during fetal development[1]. We now know that FAS is one of several disorders under the umbrella term of Fetal Alcohol Spectrum Disorder (FASD). While diagnosing any effects of prenatal exposure to alcohol has only been possible since 1973, FASD truly has been with us as long as alcohol has. As we learn about FASD, the outcomes for those affected will hopefully improve. There are now many who tirelessly advocate, thereby creating hope for those who have been affected.

FASD is the number one preventable cause of developmental, learning, and intellectual disabilities in the world[2]. It is commonly stated that FASD is *entirely* preventable. In theory, yes. While FASD is *largely* preventable, many may not agree with those who say it is entirely so. It is important to put the blame on the substance (alcohol) that causes the damage, not the vehicle (the mother). It appears to be a widely known fact that women learn of their pregnancies at various points during the pregnancy. In one conversation in this book, the mother did not know until she went into labor; in other cases, the mother chose to continue drinking after learning of the pregnancy. It is not for me, or you, the reader, to judge her or any woman, as we are not privy to the reasons for her drinking or the many other things in life she may have been wrestling with. In several of the stories, no one recognized the dangers alcohol poses to babies in the womb, and for decades, women were reassured that one glass of red wine per night was actually *good* for the baby. Today, we know better. There remains much misinformation about how much alcohol is too much and that drinking early on is "safe." Today, we know that there is no safe amount or no safe time within the pregnancy during which to drink[3]. In addition, because a developing female's eggs are formed prior to her birth if a woman is pregnant with a girl, alcohol affects not only the child but potentially also all of the mother's potential grandchildren (if alcohol was ingested at the time the eggs are formed within the female fetus). Men are not off the hook, either! A father drinking at home can make it hard for a pregnant woman who enjoys alcohol to resist. In addition, substances used (drugs or alcohol) by the father affect his sperm, which is stored for up to three months. While these changes to sperm do not cause FASD, they can impart many similar effects upon the baby through changes to either the genetic code or the epigenetic code, which affects the "copy/paste" function during cell reproduction. Think of the "do not disturb sign" hanging outside a hotel door, directing the cleaning crew to pass on by. Depending on the epigenetic marker, sections of a DNA strand may not be copy/pasted into the subsequent cells. Clearly, much emphasis needs to be on prevention. The intersection of several 2021 statistics by the National Institute for Alcohol Abuse and Alcoholism[4] is cause for concern. The NIAAA found that 78.3% of American adults drink alcohol (including 9.8% of pregnant women ages 15-44), 21.5% of Americans ages 12 and up admitted to binge drinking during the prior month (including 4.4% of pregnant women ages 15-44), and that 11.3% of all adults in the US qualified for Alcohol Use Disorder (AUD) in the year prior to their 2021 survey. According to the Centers for Disease Control and Prevention, 45% of pregnancies in the US are unplanned[5]. The NIAAA also reports *the importance of abstinence from alcohol by both parents for a minimum of three months prior to attempted conception is needed to succeed in controlling this epidemic.*

According to Dr. Anne Streisguth[6], "behaviors" can be divided into Primary Characteristics (those behaviors that directly reflect the changes to the brain's wiring) and Secondary Symptoms (those that reflect the poor fit between someone's abilities and the expectations placed upon them by others). As neuroscientists learned more, the list of Secondary Characteristics was further subdivided into Secondary and Tertiary Symptoms (when systems outside the family get involved)[7]. Primary Characteristics are the impairments in cognitive functioning – in the brain's abilities to perform the brain-tasks that underlie all outward behavior. Because we cannot see *inside* the brain, these impairments are invisible. All of us go through life with expectations of others, generally based upon social norms for our particular culture. Much of these expectations are also based upon what we have come to understand about what someone *should* be capable of doing at various ages. Expectations are placed upon us by family members, teachers, employers, teachers, therapists, peers… and even by ourselves. Because the world at large perceives behaviors as being a matter of intentional choice, those who are "wired differently" are misunderstood and judged to be doing (or not doing) things *on purpose*, and this is true for any brain-based condition. If I were to ask you, dear reader, if you have ever felt judged or marginalized, what your feelings were and the actions you instinctively wanted to take in response, chances are it would be some variation of fight, flight, or freeze. These various expressions of anxiety, anger, or withdrawal can be directed toward self, toward others, or both. All of these normal, defensive behaviors are designed to guard against the pain of further judgment and rejection. They are also the behaviors that lead to therapy referrals, where, odds are, the individual will be diagnosed with depression, oppositional defiant disorder, adjustment disorder, or others, and the behaviors will be targeted for change without consideration for why someone has the need to protect themselves from further pain. In other words, our current mental health system's goal is to eradicate someone's attempts to protect themselves without considering what the behaviors are that they cannot perform well, or at least consistently, in the first place. By identifying the source of the struggle and addressing that need, the outward behavior will extinguish itself with time, patience, and practice. This is because professionals trained in techniques inspired by Learning Theory have not yet learned to view behavior as a reflection of how well or how poorly a client can perform the brain tasks that underlie any desired behavior. According to the CDC, 90% of those with FASD have comorbid mental health issues. The most frequently diagnosed disorders include ADHD, conduct disorder, alcohol or drug dependence, depression, and anxiety[8]. Until providers understand that these behaviors are the outlets for pent-up frustration and pain, clients will continue to feel blamed, shamed, and punished for their biologically-driven behaviors.

When secondary behaviors, which are unconscious cries for help, do not elicit the support needed to meet others' expectations, those defensive behaviors become reflexive, and the "problems" seem to get bigger: truancy, crime, addictions, inability to find/keep employment, homelessness, and even suicide. Systems outside the family often become involved, whether that be from juvenile/criminal justice, social services, or others. While Primary Characteristics cannot be eradicated, both Secondary and Tertiary Symptoms can be prevented, reduced, or even eliminated. The key is in recognizing when someone has brain-based differences due to prenatal exposure to alcohol, understanding their unique strengths and challenges, and putting targeted accommodations into place to support someone in meeting their goals.

When searching for information on Fetal Alcohol Spectrum Disorder using any internet search engine, one will be bombarded by a mother lode of information that is overwhelming and that is also frequently cited devoid of context or based upon few studies. For instance, according to the CDC, youth with an FASD have a 61% higher risk of disrupted school experiences: 53% of teens had been suspended, 29% had been expelled, and 25% had dropped out[9]. The statistic is accurate but omits the context that these youth did not receive the supports they needed from school personnel, at least not in a way that was helpful. Rather, most often, they were told that "they could do it if they tried harder." Another sad statistic is that those with an FASD are 30 times more likely to have criminal justice involvement, either as teens or adults[10], although inconsistent screening has yielded a variety of statistics in this area. It is true that those with an FASD are overly represented within the criminal justice system. However, missing is the complex context of why those with FASD are vulnerable "targets" due to their people-pleasing nature, their high degree of suggestibility, and their desire to be accepted. They are often "set up" by criminals as a means of escaping prosecution themselves[11]. These are just a few of the outcomes predicted for those with an FASD. These scary outcomes are far more likely to occur to an individual if their disability is never identified. All people will do better in life when they no longer feel chronically misunderstood, marginalized, voiceless, blamed, shamed, and punished.

I've also tried to convey that FASD is not just a developmental issue, a brain-issue, a behavioral issue, or a learning/intellectual issue. It is a whole-body medical diagnosis. Alcohol affects whatever body structure is being formed at the time of exposure in terms of its anatomy and/or its functionality. Those affected by prenatal exposure to alcohol have unusually high prevalence rates for 428 other conditions[12], impacting every system of the body. We must do better at identifying those who were exposed to alcohol prior to birth. Those affected have the right to their medical history, and part of that history is the knowledge of what they may be predisposed to. Such knowledge can be invaluable when a doctor is trying to make *any* type of differential diagnosis.

Alcohol does not discriminate in its destruction. It robs the next generation of potential. In a recent article, it was noted that individuals with FASD are less capable of neuroplasticity than those not exposed to alcohol.[13] It is a worldwide health crisis that affects every country, every race, every ethnicity, every faith, and every creed.

In 2018, Dr. May conducted a study in four large metropolitan areas around the country.[14] He found that FASDs affect 1-5% of the general population, and this was determined to be a conservative estimate. Today, it is widely accepted to be 5%. If we were to apply that 5% to the 2022 US Adult population of 333+ million, we would be flabbergasted to learn there are well over 16.6 million adults in our midst living with the effects of prenatal alcohol exposure. For children, 5% of the 80.4 million would be 4+ million children.

One of the ways in which people coped with the Covid-19 pandemic and associated lockdowns was by turning to alcohol. Alcohol sales immediately rose by 20% and have remained at that higher level[15], even though the lockdowns are a thing of the past. According to an article in The Hill on 6/12/23, *Americans are drinking as much alcohol now as in the Civil War days*; compared to the mid-1990s, Americans are drinking 60% more hard liquor and 50% more wine (though 15% less beer).[16] It goes without saying that we are headed for a crisis. It has been shown that people who have ACEs (Adverse Childhood Experiences) are more likely to have FASD and that those who have FASD are more likely to have ACEs.[17]

The stories within this book are as unique as the people who so generously shared their vulnerability as well as their time. There remains a stigma against FASD,[18, 19]even though those living with it did nothing to bring it about. It is what it is; we are all given only one life to live, and we must make the best of it as we can. Though details vary widely, there are many commonalities. The conversations transcribed in this book are shared with you, the reader, in an effort to show what FASD can look like in adults. Almost all conversations in this book are with individuals who discovered as adults how their lives make much more sense after understanding how prenatal exposure to alcohol has affected them. The nine people I spoke with in this book, and a few others, were either referred to me or people that I heard on podcasts or were active on social media sites for FASD. These conversations were not scripted, though the theme was the same: discuss what it was like to pursue and receive a diagnosis, what the impact of that was, and what the individuals are doing to benefit the cause of FASD Awareness. The recorded conversations were transcribed by AI and edited solely for readability (for example, written vs. conversational English). I was not able to include the transcript of every conversation due to the constraints of space (I only paid for a certain number of pages).

In the Appendix, I offer resources for your further learning and support: websites, books, podcasts, support groups, and more. If you choose to seek professional support as you embark on this journey of self-discovery, please do what you can to ensure that the provider understands that FASD is a cause of neurodivergence. In essence, it is caused by a pre-birth brain injury. Rewards and consequences can result in short-term compliance but not lasting change. I highly recommend working with a Certified Facilitator of the FASCETS Neurobehavioral Model, whether me or someone else, who can walk you through methodically exploring your unique strengths and preferred learning style as well as your unique challenges. At Patricia Kasper, MA MTh, Training Services, LLC, I train professionals in this model to increase the base of support available to individuals and families, and I have two four-month programs, one for parents of children affected by prenatal alcohol exposure and other neurobehavioral conditions, and one for adults, such as yourself, who may resonate with the following stories, and are wondering, "What now?"

My Story

In 2017, I had been working at a child welfare non-profit agency for nearly two decades. My passion for adding more tools to my own toolbox had led me to attend workshops and in-depth trainings led by some of this nation's experts in adoption issues, child development, attachment, trauma, and more. In 2018, the agency was awarded a contract with the county for post-adoption support services, and I immediately applied. While I provided adoption and trauma-specific education to parents in adoption home study writing process, this new program would enable me to grow my platform. Part of the contract was to provide training not only to the agency's adoptive families but to families and professionals within the community as well. Stepping into this role, I was thrilled to have a greater reach in imparting such knowledge to those entrusted with bringing stability and healing to children who have undergone significantly more grief and loss than any child should and whose parents were deemed incapable of caring for their children. This led me to discover my passion for training. I am as passionate about equipping professionals to better support those with whom they work as I am about educating parents to be sources of healing for their children.

Two months into my new role, which included facilitating a monthly support group, I asked a friend who had previously adopted three children diagnosed with Fetal Alcohol Spectrum Disorder to present to those who attended the group. She was accompanied by one of her friends, whose adopted children had been diagnosed with Fetal Alcohol Syndrome, which is one of the diagnoses under the "umbrella" of FASD. They did a great presentation and provided a valuable perspective on the behaviors our group members struggled with routinely. They also planted the seeds of what would change my life. Two years later, my friend passed along a flyer for training on FASD.

I learned about FASCETS (Fetal Alcohol Spectrum Consultation, Education, and Training Services) as a resource to deepen my understanding on a professional level. I signed up for the twelve-hour workshop, where I was introduced to various tools used in the Neurobehavioral Model. I found it curious that many of the challenges common to those who have brain-based conditions, including FASD, were behaviors that had been challenges in my own life. There was a group exercise designed to normalize neurodiversity – the reality that no two people think alike. The group was assigned to have our family members do the exercise and compare our creations. I had my mother do the exercise because she lives with my husband and I. My husband walked through the room while I was talking with my mother and commented jokingly, "So that's what's wrong with you." His comment prompted me to ask my mother if she consumed alcohol while she was pregnant with me. Her answer? "Oh yeah, every day!" It was, after all, the early 60s, more than a decade prior to the "discovery" of Fetal Alcohol Syndrome.

Mic drop!

It was as if someone had taken all the cards from my deck of life, reshuffled them, and given them back to me. All of a sudden, I knew why I resonated with what I had been learning in my classes with FASCETS. All of a sudden, I understood why the explanations I always believed for the "whys" in my life didn't really explain things that well – things about myself that had long-frustrated me as well as those around me.

For instance, one of my mother's favorite stories to tell from when I was a baby was that it would take me hours to nurse a decent amount of milk. I now know the reason for this. Many who have been prenatally exposed to alcohol experience deficits in their suckling response.[20]

Throughout childhood, I experienced rejection by nearly everyone. For instance, I was the kid that the team captains fought over as to who would get "stuck" with me. I was the kid whose few friends paid the price for befriending me by losing their other friends. I was the kid to be invited to a sleepover at the cool girl's house for the sole purpose of being used as the guinea pig in a malicious game of truth or dare. While kids' propensity to be cruel to other kids deemed "different" was not new to me, I now knew that my "differentness" was not because I was the only diabetic in school or the smallest kid in my grade[21], but in reality, because I was neurodivergent due to my prenatal exposure to alcohol.

Other odd things about my childhood began to float up to my consciousness as I began to process the reality that my life had been negatively impacted by prenatal exposure to alcohol. When I was very young, I had difficulty understanding that I could love all my family members at the same time. I now know that one common effect of prenatal exposure to alcohol is difficulty processing abstract concepts.[22]Another common challenge associated with prenatal alcohol exposure is related to memory and the ability to do things in the proper sequence of steps. If a person struggles with either brain task, the results will be disappointing.[23]

I came to recognize several other common struggles during my transitional-age years, which for me actually began a few years earlier than most when I entered college at the age of sixteen. During the course of my college years, I changed my major, and my college, numerous times before finally graduating with a bachelor's degree in social work in 1987. My frequent change of majors is a perfect example of not being able to finish what I had begun, another classic example of FASD challenges.[24]Yes, I am one of "those people" who gets very distracted by the things I pick up in order to put them away while cleaning a room. Others struggle to initiate tasks (i.e., procrastination) because they are so leery of doing something poorly that they would rather avoid it altogether, or they don't know where to start because there are so many steps. Yes, I am also one of "those people."

A frequent misperception is that people with FASD are stupid; they are not. With all my challenges, I went on to complete three graduate degrees. And yet, memory has been a challenge, and indeed, had led to a change in majors away from nursing.[25]

Another common effect of prenatal alcohol exposure is an addiction to sugar. Because alcohol is metabolized as a sugar, those of us who had alcohol pumping through our bodies throughout our early development were "set up" for addiction by the sudden withdrawal of it at the time of our births. Having believed for decades, it was a psychological reaction to being told what I should and shouldn't eat because of the diabetes. I now know that my addiction to sugar had a biological basis rather than a psychological one.

Another unhappy struggle that faces many of us who were prenatally exposed to alcohol is difficulties in relationships. While other things factor in, such as a history of trauma, attachment issues, or being from a broken home, part of it also has to do with having a poor "social IQ." Many people with FASD have challenges with reading body or facial language or being able to discern the true intent of others. Most with FASD are people-pleasers and value the perception of approval or affection above numerous other values. This leads to a myriad of challenges and can place many at risk of victimization.[26]During my undergraduate years, that meant I was never without a boyfriend, much to the chagrin of my parents. That pattern was broken by my unhappy marriage that lasted five years. Due to the above reasons, I was very vulnerable following my divorce. One year after my separation, a predator swept me off my feet, but during that painful time, I was protected, I believe, by the Hand of God. I now know that people who have been prenatally exposed to alcohol are very vulnerable to predators due to compromised social judgment or poor social IQ. The good news is that poor social judgment as a child, teen, or young adult, is not necessarily permanent and that dysmaturity, or delayed social/emotional maturation, generally resolves in one's mid-thirties.

Like others featured in this book, learning about FASD and its implications for my life has been a journey of self-discovery. While I always had explanations for my struggles in life, deep down, the explanations didn't seem sufficient. Looking back at my life through the lens of FASD has made infinitely more sense.

I now constantly use a phrase I learned at FASCETS, which is, "None of us knew what we didn't know... until we learned it." We each have different life experiences, backgrounds, interests, and talents. As we are exposed to new information, for example, when listening to a sermon or a lecture, different aspects of the material will take hold of us and make an indelible impact. Learning about the complexities of brain injuries caused by prenatal exposure to alcohol has that effect. Once you learn it, it *will* change you.

The training three years ago at FASCETS profoundly changed me on both a personal level and a professional level. I completed a second workshop with FASCETS and then spent one year with the organization, becoming a Certified Facilitator of their Neurobehavioral Model. My career was forever changed as I realized the impact of prenatal alcohol exposure on all the children I had cared for, worried about, and watched fall through the cracks. I learned that alcohol literally changes a baby's brain structure, altering the way that it functions in such a way that what others expect should be easy for a child to do can be difficult at best and impossible at worst. These children then had been failed by the system that was supposed to protect them because no one realized these same children had invisible disabilities. They had brain injuries prior to birth that forever altered the course of their development. Why had I not known this? My agency didn't know. The county social workers didn't know. The mental health system of care didn't address this either. All the systems I interacted with presumed that children chose their behavior intentionally. Behavior management, then, is a matter of choosing the right incentive or threatening the right negative consequence for the child to be motivated to make the desired choice and change their behavior. If the variety of bribes or punishments were ineffective, the parents were deemed to be undermining the prescribed approach, or the child was deemed incorrigible and moved as often as needed to keep people from quitting as foster parents. Except you cannot bribe or punish away the effects of a brain injury.

This assumption about behavior – that it can be targeted for change using rewards and consequences – is a view widely held by every aspect of societies all over the world. It is so widely accepted that few questions if it is accurate, much like the once widely-held belief that the world was flat. It is, in short, a paradigm; specifically, it is the behavior paradigm. It is also, actually, wrong. Neuroscience has proven it to be wrong over the course of the past twenty years. This material, as with adoption issues, trauma, and attachment, is not learned in graduate school. The interested professional must seek it out. Most colleges and universities continue to teach up-and-coming doctors, lawyers, teachers, therapists, social workers, childcare workers (and more) that behavior is intentional because that is what is widely believed. They cannot teach what they themselves have not yet learned. This is why, if the professionals to whom you've turned for help don't seem to "get" you or your child, you have not gotten the support you have desperately needed. You, and your family, deserve better.

What I learned as I dove into the study of FASD also shifted my understanding of the struggle that birth parents face in their efforts to regain custody of their children. If we accept that drug and alcohol use is often a behavioral pattern that is passed from one generation down to the next, it is not enough to recognize the child's struggles as being the result of prenatal toxins. Those parents were also likely exposed to toxins, such as alcohol, drugs, or chronically high cortisol levels, prior to their own births. This means that the "simple" tasks assigned to them by social workers and caseworkers may, in fact, be incredibly challenging or impossible due to the unrecognized cognitive impairments of the birth parents, as they may also have unrecognized invisible disabilities.

The use of alcohol is widely accepted across nearly every aspect of our society. One cannot watch an hour of television during prime time without seeing several advertisements for alcohol. The statistics I included in the Prologue are prior to the lockdowns of the Covid pandemic. Still, 5% equals one in twenty people. That means one or two students in every classroom, several residents on every block of every street, one in twenty of your coworkers, and one in twenty of the folks with you in your house of worship. With the pandemic came the sad reality that alcohol consumption among women also rose. Think about what that means for classrooms beginning with the school year of 2025-2026. It implies that probably two children in each classroom will be blamed and shamed for not being able to sit still, regulate their emotions or behavior, keep their hands to themselves, or manage being over-stimulated while simultaneously paying attention to what the teachers are saying (spoiler alert: it is rarely possible for an entire school day)… and the list of struggles goes on. Their underlying invisible disabilities will continue to go unrecognized or supported until we, as a society, learn to view behaviors differently and until we, as a society, accept that all children will do well if they are able to.

We often fail to consider the role of prenatal alcohol exposure because drinking is so widely accepted and because the behavioral characteristics of other, more familiar diagnoses overlap with the behavioral characteristics of FASD. Oftentimes, because the stigma of FASD is real, a provider may suggest that using the other, more common diagnoses will be "good enough" to access services without adding a stigmatizing label. Except those other diagnoses are not associated with 428 comorbid conditions that can affect every bodily system. A true and accurate diagnosis is important. Let me state for the record that I have not yet pursued obtaining a formal diagnosis of FASD due to self-identifying enough of the characteristics in combination with my mother's admission that she had consumed alcohol on a daily basis during her pregnancy with me. In this, I am in the same boat as many of my readers; self-identification verified by parental reports.

The stories in this book are as unique as the individuals I converse with. This is fitting because no two people are affected by FASD in the same way, not even twins. It is this wide variance that makes the identification of FASD so challenging. This book is not yet another means of foisting blame upon our parents for our miseries, but rather, it is about the intense psychological sense of relief that comes from understanding the biological basis of our quirks, behaviors, and struggles. It is about raising much-needed awareness.

FASD Looks Like Me
A Conversation with Gina Schumaker

In this conversation, I speak with Gina Schumaker, who is a self-advocate, board member of the Alaska Center for FASD and a FASD speaker. She recently joined the International Adult Leadership Collaborative of the FASD Changemakers. Gina also stages homes for the real estate industry.

Patti: Hi, Gina. I'd really love for you to tell me a little bit about your journey. What led you to seek an FASD diagnosis?

Gina: I was out with girlfriends and told one of the girls that I thought I had an FASD, and she said, "Gina, there's no way - look at you! You can't have FASD!" Well, I had previously been at my son's school, where a lady complained about how difficult it was to raise four children with FASD. I looked at her, then I looked at them, and it hit me that you don't have to look a certain way (to have FASD). I had thought the native (American) culture was the only culture that suffered from FASD. I didn't really know that it affected me as well. But my friend who had said I couldn't have it later invited me to attend a presentation by Billy Edwards. He's an attorney and was speaking at the local Bar Association, coincidentally, about FASD. Within five minutes, she looked over at me and, (knowing my family history), she apologized and said, "I'm sorry, you have it."

So from then, it's kind of been a little bit of a roller coaster. I went to get a neuropsych evaluation, and the first neuropsychologist told me that my FASD "wasn't bad enough to diagnose." And I said, "Just because I'm not native doesn't mean that I don't deserve to get a diagnosis. You've never seen a 50-year-old white woman in here." That's why I kind of got a little bit pissy with him, and he admitted you do have FASD, but your PTSD is far worse than your FASD." I said I had never been in a war, and he said, "You've been in four wars, Gina," (referring to my trauma history). I did nothing with the information for a year out of my anger at his resistance to giving me a diagnosis; he didn't understand a diagnosis was necessary for me to be an effective advocate for those with FASD.

Well, I reached out to (a professional in Soldotna, Alaska) who said that I needed to come down there, which is two and a half hours away, and see them for a diagnosis. They did their own workup. When I got done with the testing, she and the doctor sat down and talked with me. They confirmed my FASD diagnosis and told me exactly what my issues (challenges) were and what my strengths were, and what I needed help with.

That led to me making a decision to reach out and help other people. So I reached out to the Alaska Center for FASD, and I asked them about getting on their board (of directors). It is a state-wide resource for individuals, families, caregivers and professionals who want to know more about FASD, including navigating systems, referrals to supports and services, outreach and awareness. It's been a great relationship. I'm so glad I joined their board.

Patti: Let me stop you there, Gina. I can tell you just gave me the cliff notes version. I know there's so much that I missed in that. So at the beginning of what you just shared with me, you knew you had FASD. You were fifty at the time. Tell me what led you to that conclusion, and what were you struggling with that made you even wonder about it?

Gina: So I knew some things were not working in my life. I knew I needed to figure it out. When I talked with that mom in my son's school, it was the moment I knew. I wasn't good with money, math, time management, or the passage of time.[27] To be quite honest, I always believed that if I was a "good enough" girl, was friendly enough, bubbly enough, or happy enough... that I'd be okay.

Patti: All of those things (money, time, and math) are abstract concepts. Those are classical things that folks with FASDs struggle with. What other impacts do you now recognize as being tied to FASD?

Gina: I struggle with interpersonal relationships. I've been married four times. The relationship I'm in now has lasted over 20 years. But it's still a struggle. Relationships are really hard with anybody, male or female.

Patti: Relationships are hard for people who are neurotypical too. But how much more so for those of us who may struggle with non-verbal communication – facial expressions, body language, voice tone, and cadence?[28]

Gina: People have taken advantage of me a lot because I'm gullible; many of us are. I think too communication is difficult for us. We are resilient, though, which is a positive. I think there are a lot of people out there who have it much worse than we do, so I don't really consider myself to have a disability. I think I have a different ability. I don't dwell on what I can't do. My issues around money and time are part of life. You don't have to excel in these areas, but just be decent at them. But I know that "disability" is just the way our society works.

Patti: That's true. Society has focused on disability over differences for decades. Let's talk a bit about the language of being "differently-abled" rather than "disabled." With FASD, there is a broad range of physical, cognitive, and emotional effects. No two people are the same; some, like me, function very well, overall, while others will never be capable of living independently. In addition, because the verbal expression is often within the "normal range," most people don't realize that someone may have no clue what is being asked of them or that they might not be able to read or write.[29] The standard measurement of intelligence is the IQ score (even though it was never meant to be used that way), and among those with FASD, IQ ranges from 20 all the way to 130. But you and I know that FASD is not just about intellect. There's tremendous variation in adaptive function, or the ability to function in life. You can have an IQ of 130 and still need help with activities of daily living.[30]

Gina: Absolutely. I don't know why they call it common sense because common sense is not very common. I have good life skills. I think that being resilient goes a long way too, and I'm doing okay with the hand I was dealt. You have to do good to *be* good. That's what matters. I just know that without my church, without the people that love me, I wouldn't be here. I went through (a time when) I had suicidal ideation and had planned out when and how I was going to do it. I was 19 years old. I got a gun. I got everything, and I lay there. I prayed, and then it hit me: if I killed myself, then God was going to be mad at me. So I decided I better not do that because I wanted to go to heaven. That wasn't my first risky situation, or the first time I knew God protected me. I had been hitchhiking since I was 13, drinking a lot, and making bad choices. But I had believed that if I hitchhiked to go to work, then God would protect me. But if I hitchhiked to do bad things, He might not. That was my rationalization. God did have His hand upon me. People (who picked me up) would take me to the door of where I worked and would sometimes pick me up after work and take me home because they had been worried about me. I lived in Florida in those days. Those were very dangerous times then. But we are resilient people, and knowing now that I have FASD has helped me quite a bit to put the puzzle pieces together. For so long, I struggled with knowing who I was or why I was the way I was. I always felt like something was wrong with me. I no longer feel that way.

Patti: So there are so many different things that can lead someone to be neurodivergent. What made you look at FASD?

Gina: Well, I knew my mom was a heavy drinker; I just hadn't known that I was affected by it. I didn't know it had anything to do with me. At doctor appointments, on the intake forms, there would be questions about it, so I answered that yes, she was a heavy drinker. But no one ever told me I had FASD.

Patti: How old were you at that point?

Gina: I started seeing him (a psychiatrist) when I was 42. I recognized I had the characteristics of ADHD, which he confirmed and started me on Adderall. I saw him every three months, but he didn't really know what to

4

do with me (beyond medication management). So I had been seeing him for about eight years when I finally realized that I probably had FASD. He was really receptive to it but clarified my diagnosis under that umbrella is FAE (Fetal Alcohol Effects, a diagnostic term no longer used). He said that I should probably seek counselling, but I couldn't find a therapist with the appropriate knowledge base. Like most people, therapists in my area had a lot of misinformation about needing certain facial characteristics and seemed surprised that adults have FASD too. They only provided counselling to children.

Patti: The bit about where you don't have "the face." So many people are not diagnosed because they don't have facial changes. They don't have small eye openings, a super thin upper lip or a flat (and sometimes elongated) philtrum, or the space between the lip and the nose.

Gina: Right.

Patti: So, you and I know that you only get "the face" if alcohol was consumed between days 17 and 21. There is misinformation that if you have facial features, you have "the worst" kind of FASD. But no. It only means that you were exposed to alcohol when a specific type of cell that becomes the face is being formed. Alcohol affects whatever body structure or function happens to be developing at the time of exposure. So outside of those five days, there is a whole range of damage being done to the baby. In fact, there are 428 conditions that have an elevated prevalence rate among those with an FASD compared with the general population! It is a whole-body diagnosis tied to the damage done no matter which day of pregnancy, including those days prior to a woman discovering she is pregnant. That saying, "Drink till it's pink," has led to hundreds of thousands of people with damage to their brains and bodies.

Gina: So my mom drank heavily and didn't know she was pregnant with me. Her doctors actually thought she had a tumor and shipped her up to Colorado to have (me) removed. They didn't have an ultrasound back then. When they opened her up, they found me and closed her back up again. But

5

when she went back home, she didn't tell anybody she was pregnant and kept drinking. She didn't have me for another three months.

Patti: So do you have brothers and sisters?

Gina: I do, but both my brother and sister are deceased. At the time, no one recognized the impact of alcohol on them either, but looking back, it is clear. My older sister and I had very different childhoods because she was raised by my grandmother and so grew up in a more stable environment. My brother and I had very little supervision.

Patti: So you grew up in Florida?

Gina: I grew up in Colorado until I was 10. That's when my mom married someone in the military and we moved to Florida, where he was stationed. I lived in Florida for 15 years.

Patti: You started hitchhiking at 13 to go to work and school?

Gina: I would take the bus to school and then hitchhike to work. My mom kicked me out when I was 16. So I didn't have much of a relationship with her after that. I slept in the woods for three nights, but a lady at the food store didn't like that, so she asked me to move in with her and watch her kids at night while she worked. That worked for a while until one of the neighbors turned her in because they thought she was taking advantage of me. When the police talked to my mom, she reported me as a runaway so that she wouldn't get in trouble for throwing me out at 16. I had never been in trouble before but found myself in a detention center. I did smoke a little bit of pot and drink a little bit of beer back then, but not much. After the detention center, I moved back in with my mother, but not for long. She had taken the keys to the car I bought with my pay checks. She was angry with me for not doing the dishes. I hadn't done them because it was my brother's turn, but he was stoned and sleeping. She told me she was going to sell my car. We got into a huge fight. When I went out to get my school books out of my car, she locked the door on me, and I couldn't get back in. So I slept in the woods again. So anyway, long story short, I was dating a guy – I wasn't even that interested in him or sexually active with him - but when his dad found out that I slept in the woods, he freaked out and paid for us to move into an apartment together. So I was able to have a nice apartment, go to school and work part-time. It wasn't horrible.

Patti: So you weren't in love, but you knew that was a good arrangement.

Gina: Yeah. It was survival. We were young. We made it work, until he hit me. So I left. Patti, they say if he hits you once, he's going to hit you twice. So I moved out. I was smart. I knew what to do there.

Patti: If we look back to our coming-of-age years and our capacity to make good judgments, in hindsight, we recognize the impact of FASD in those years. We had excellent judgment in some things but were incredibly foolish in other areas. Judgment is hit or miss, just like (social and emotional) maturity.

Gina: That's a great way of putting it because you just never know which one you're going to be cursed with. And I've always struggled with memory.

Patti: Memory is impacted by so many things – I've had trouble with word-finding, but low blood sugar kills brain cells, too, so it could be either diabetes or the FASD. It could also be the fact that I'm juggling so many projects while I also care full time for my mom. But overall, I'm happy with where I am. I'm being productive in building my business, and I'm making good choices. I'm relatively healthy and have been happily married for twenty-three years.

Gina: Me too, and I'm working out five or six days a week. I feel good. I keep my stress levels down by going for walks, which is therapeutic for me. I never thought I would be that person who craves exercise! I've been watching The Chosen, and I am in a Bible study on Monday nights, and we watch it as a group and talk about it. We took a break for a bit, but I wanted to watch it ahead of time because it's so good, and I'm enjoying it. So I watch it while I work out at the gym. I get three or four miles walked during each episode.

Patti: That's great! So you're finding out that FASD did fit your history and explained so much for you. It sounds like that was a relief.

Gina: I'm doing better. I was so relieved to know what it was and to not beat myself up anymore. Now I have started to give myself grace. I find tricks to help myself. For example, I have not locked my keys in the car since I was diagnosed. My car is old and can still lock with the keys inside it. So that's a win. And then another really cool thing was that I happened to buy a purse for a friend, the one who had said I didn't have FASD, but after looking at it more, I decided to keep it for myself. There's a place for keys, credit cards, for money. It helped me be organized in a way most purses never did for me. I fell in love with it. Oh my gosh. I did put things right back after using them. Through the years, I had lost driver's licenses, credit cards, and IDs. You know how it is, putting them in different places. I realized this wallet was a godsend. I told her, "I'm sorry I bought you a purse, but I have to keep it as it has been so good for my brain." I used it until it fell apart. I would love to find a purse like that again. I would market them for women with FASD.

Patti: I'm always jealous of people that can use small compact purses like that. I have to carry everything but the kitchen sink because of my diabetes.

Gina: I get that. In Alaska, we use our coat pockets a lot because we wear our coats most of the year. Lipstick, whatever. I even carry a measuring tape around with me because I'm a stager.

8

Patti: Really?

Gina: Yes, I've staged over 600 homes. Remember I said I was in a documentary? They filmed me for 8 Keys for Adults with FASD while I was in the middle of staging a house. But (FASD has affected me here too) — I've been taken advantage of several times because I don't have customers sign contracts. I stage the houses *really* nicely; I go above and beyond. I have had real estate agents keep my things.

Patti: You don't use contracts?

Gina: I've never used contracts. I've done over 600 houses without a contract. Contracts, for me, are overwhelming. They're just too much to even think about.

Patti: So, is there someone that could help you with that?

Gina: Not really. I don't ask (for help) very well. It's another one of my FASD things. Besides, I don't know anybody that would really be gifted in that area.

Patti: Maybe something simple like, "I will stage your house. I will deliver furnishings and décor and will have an itemized list of everything. After your house sells, I get everything back except those pieces you choose to purchase from me. And you both sign. That's a contract.

Gina: Yeah. That wouldn't be bad. Look at you. You're so cute, wanting to save me.

Patti: I'm not saving you, just thinking out loud about how I can make your life a little smoother.

Gina: Yeah. This conversation is very comfortable. You're very comforting. We have so much in common. When you said your mom had dementia, I could relate. I know how hard that is and the progression. My grandfather may have had dementia. Back then, they just thought he was a crazy old man. He was supposed to be our caregiver. That didn't happen. As children, we became his caretaker. Mom lived with different men. And so our grandfather was the only consistent adult around, except how consistent could he be with the dementia?

Patti: Exactly. Not very. So my mom's diagnosis is Lewy Body Dementia, which makes Alzheimer's look like a walk in the park. Learning the Neurobehavioral Model has helped me *so* much as my mother's care partner. With FASD, that's one thing I wish parents, teachers, counsellors, and social workers knew: a classic characteristic of brain-based conditions is inconsistent performance. With FASD, you can do things one day and the next day not remember or even recognize that you could do it before. That's what causes so much anxiety in folks with FASD – each day, kids wake up and wonder if they will be praised for all their hard work or if they will be punished for forgetting something. Grown-ups too. That's why things are so confusing, really, for both conditions. That's why it's so critical to be able to identify the brain (or cognitive) tasks that make any behavior (action) possible and understanding which types of brain tasks are challenging. It might be processing information from our sensory system. It might be the way our body uses nutrition. It might be the ability to process abstract concepts or executive functioning, on and on and on. Learning this really helped me be able to figure her out, and to provide tailored assistance, just like I do with parents of neurodivergent children and with neurodivergent adults, who, like us, never understood until later in life why life had been so full of challenges.

When I found the FASCETS training, and it rocked my world. As I was going through the exploration tool, I saw myself.

Gina: Mm-hmm.

Patti: I recognized all my quirks. You mentioned to me about time that you always try to be early, just in case. Well, I've always thought of myself as an "ish person." I'm naturally within a 10-minute window behind schedule. Sometimes I joke that I will find a way to be late for my own funeral. It's something I have had to work hard at. It's definitely one of my FASD effects. Like many, I underestimate how long it will take to accomplish things. Not only that but if I'm doing something, I lose all track of time. That's something that the children I've worked with in the foster care system really struggle with. Their foster parents get so frustrated because they view the child's behavior (of not getting ready or not finishing an activity) as intentional, as non-compliance, or defiance. They'll complain, "I gave all these warnings." But the reality is that it's not just that the children are engrossed in their activity. They literally have no concept that time is marching on while they're occupied with whatever. So FASCETS literally changed my life: on a personal and a professional level. I got to reshuffle the deck of cards that I was dealt, and all of a sudden, my quirks, my foibles, and the bad choices I made in my coming-of-age years made sense. But I also came to realize that all the children I had worked with who have fallen through the cracks did so because they had an invisible physical disability. It doesn't matter what the cause is, but when something changes the structure of our brains because they are a physical organ that directs the activity of every other aspect of our being, our behavior – the way we function – automatically changes too. By definition, then, FASD is a physical disability with behavioral symptoms. A disability that happens to be invisible because only 10% of those on the spectrum were born with the tell-tale facial features, and it's important to remember that as we age, our faces change, and those physical signs often disappear.

Gina: Yeah, it's a physical disability, and people don't think of FASD as that. It is a brain injury – brain damage – that occurred prior to birth. We have to play up the disability side in order to get the services that we desperately need, but at the same time, really emphasize that just because you have FASD, you can still do things. You do have strengths. You do have gifts and talents. And you can do some things better because of the challenges you have.

Patti: Yes, it revolutionized my practice as a social worker. I began to train the staff and parents at the company I worked for. That doesn't feel like enough of a reach, though – I want to be more of a catalyst for change than that, so now I'm in business for myself as a trainer for professionals and as a coach for both parents and neurodivergent adults.

Gina: I would love to do something like that. I'd like to learn more about (myself in that way). I'd also love to become a trainer about FASD too.

Patti: (smiling) I know someone who can help you with that. If you are interested in becoming a Certified Facilitator of the FASCETS Neurobehavioral Model, I can take you through all the pre-requisite training.

Gina: That would be awesome. I would love that. I'd love to be better prepared to raise awareness up here. I've done a lot of zoom during COVID to help nurses and doctors, and students learn about FASD and answer their questions.

Have you seen the movie Moment to Moment? I didn't care for it when I saw it, but later realized it was because I never had the support the teens in the movie had, and I was envious. I was disappointed that it was all about teens and didn't show anything about how adults with FASD function. I think it'd be awesome to do one for adults. I would love to be in it. I would love to let people walk a day in my shoes.

Patti: That would be interesting. So if someone could spend a day in your shoes... what is one thing about FASD that you really want people to understand?

Gina: I think the most important thing that I would like people to understand is that FASD is very different for everybody. FASD is an umbrella of different effects. People don't think of us like that. They think of autism like that. But the FASD umbrella is just as big or bigger. Certainly, there are more of us. I think knowing that because many of us struggle with time, changing the clocks forward and back can create a lot of challenges for us. I want people to know that things we know today might not be remembered tomorrow; we can and do learn, but with some things, it may take longer.

Patti: Have you always experienced that struggle?

Gina: Yes.

Patti: Did that create anxiety in you as a child?

Gina: I've only been diagnosed with an anxiety (disorder) for a year, but looking back, I've always had it. I realized that I had been self-medicating anxiety with alcohol and cannabis, using it to calm down because even exercise wouldn't relieve my stress. My neck and back were always a hot mess – it's where I carry my stress. I hear people every day talk about anxiety, but the "freak out kind." But mine is an internal kind that I think can be almost worse. It's like I'm trying to hold it together, and at the same time, I'm paralyzed. For instance, my bedroom is a total disaster - you can barely walk in it. I want to organize and clean it, but I just get paralyzed by certain things. But then, I'm a perfectionist. But I get anxious even thinking about trying.

Patti: Many of us are perfectionists, and that's why we don't start anything or follow through with anything because we can't. We get stuck. Trouble initiating or completing things with multiple steps can be very hard for many of us – it's a brain thing.

Gina: And because we're afraid we won't get it or won't do it perfectly, we avoid it.

Patti: We're afraid we won't be able to finish, so we avoid starting. In Autism circles, this is often referred to as Persistent Demand Avoidance, or PDA, but it affects many of us with FASD as well. I know it does me. Or we start but happily move on to the next shiny object to avoid what we're making ourselves try to complete. For many, for things that need to be done regularly, the question then becomes, "What's the point?" This struggle is actually something that falls under executive function. I can relate with you because I've always hated cleaning. Always. I do it, but I hate it. Sometimes I get in the overwhelmed state with it too. My favorite hack to help with this is an app called Fly Lady.

Gina: Yes, we're all still learning and growing. I feel like I've matured more in the last ten years than I ever have.

Patti: It's why my unofficial company slogan is that we're all diamonds in the rough – I hope I never stop learning and growing.

Gina: I think I've gotten wiser, and I enjoy myself more in general now. With ADHD, getting on Adderall helped me quite a bit with focus.

Patti: So, now that you are settled and have embraced FASD as the explanation for your struggles in life, what are you doing to pay it forward to the rest of us, so to speak?

Gina: I serve the FASD population by being an advocate for others and speaking out, and by talking about different programs. I did a podcast with Robbie Seal (FASD Family Life). That was fun. I like to do things that help give people hope. I want people to understand that you are going to be okay. (As a parent or teacher or whatever,) know that your kid is going to be okay. You don't want to enable that child. You want to help that child be the best version of themselves that they can be. By doing so, you will create a good individual. I think that that's an important thing. I think you have to realize that it's not all hum and drum. I don't know if you watched my YouTube. I made a YouTube video on my FASD four years ago. I need to do another one because I have people actually contact me privately and ask me to do more videos. Because in the video, I say that just because you have an FASD doesn't mean you're going to be homeless or on drugs.

Patti: Or in prison, per internet searches.

Gina: Yes, that bothers me too. I have gone through my own share of bad choices, but I own them. I realized many of those bad choices were because I was self-medicating. I think I always knew that I had been self-medicating from a very young age, but I wasn't sure why. FASD gave me the answer as to why.

Patti: I'm hoping that this book does that for people - that people will pick this (book) up out of curiosity if nothing else. They'll read our stories and wonder if this explains their life too. It is so revolutionary to all of a sudden have an explanation for our bad choices, for years of rejection, of misunderstandings of a variety of our struggles. But with an explanation that fits. Like looking back at the many changes of majors and colleges in my life – starting college at 16 and being too young to know what I wanted to do was certainly an explanation, but knowing that FASD makes finishing things challenging is a big piece of it too! I know that you're on the board of the Alaska Center for FASD. What all does that organization do?

Gina: We do outreach. We were connected to an FASD diagnosis team, though that part of the organization went under due to limited funding. But we stood strong and got five new board members. Alaska Center for FASD was actually founded by Marilyn Pierce-Bulger, and she's still involved as a volunteer. Her ongoing involvement is helpful. She's a nurse practitioner and has done a lot in our community for FASD. We do awareness walks and like to do things in the community to help others. We also put on talks with doctors and nurses and such.

Patti: That's wonderful.

Gina: We do what we can to help. The movie I told you about was one of our projects, so that is exciting. Its release date is September 8, 2023.

Patti: Very exciting. Is it a documentary or docudrama of someone's story?

Gina: It's a short film that has some animation in it. It is "8 Keys for Adults with FASD." The original 8 Magic Keys was entirely animated. The videographer did an awesome job editing and creating animated segments. The movie is 30 minutes long but should be effective in showing everyone that no one outgrows FASD and that it is a spectrum; there is a full range of effects. Raising awareness is what it's all about.

Patti: How very fun! So you educate a lot of the medical professionals in your area.

Gina: Yes.

Patti: It is astounding to me how misinformed the medical and therapeutic community is about FASD. I get it for when our parents were young and having children – because FAS was "discovered" as a "thing" only 50 years ago. But now? It is incredulous to me that we still have doctors and nurses and midwives saying, "oh yeah, you can have a drink when you're pregnant - just one glass of red wine. You'll be fine." That blows my mind. I'm curious how prevalent do you find that issue to be up there in Alaska?

Gina: Oh, very prevalent. It seems that their education about FASD is just outdated. We educate people whenever we're doing community service. I don't know what you call it in your town, but our CPC (Community Service Patrol) helps with the people that get drunk and fall or pass out by picking them up and taking them to "the drunk tank to sober up." We want to do a class for the CPC and educate them, and help them because I guarantee 90% of those they assist are homeless or have FASD. Similarly, the rate of those incarcerated with FASD is disproportionately high.

Patti: That is very true. The tragedy is that it doesn't have to be that way. With early identification and supportive accommodations in place, tragic outcomes like homelessness, incarceration, and suicide can be prevented! Dr. May's classic study in 2017 shows that the prevalence of FASD in the general population is 5% - that's one in every 20 people. To put it another way, a minimum of one child in every classroom! But what happened in response to the Covid Lockdowns? Alcohol sales increased by 20%, with women drinking at the increased rate of 41 percent! Alcohol sales have stayed at that higher sales point even though the lockdowns have gone away. Without people recognizing the serious toll of prenatal alcohol exposure, we're going to have a real epidemic on our hands!

Gina: 5% was a *conservative* estimate. From the data I've looked at, I'd say it's more like 1:15. With the higher alcohol usage when all the children born since 2020 turn five years old and begin school, the schools aren't going to know what to do. They already don't know what to do. Personally, I would like to have routine screening for FASD as part of enrollment into kindergarten. I also think screening at birth should be automatic.

Patti: Alcohol screening is available, but it's a different screening tool than what's used for drugs and is more expensive. From my experience in child welfare, I would say that women are not admitting to using alcohol because they're already forced to admit to things that the toxicology screenings indicated. Why also admit to alcohol, which is legal?

Gina: Mm-hmm. The reason why is for the sake of the baby - for early intervention.

Patti: Well, yes. But remember how many mixed messages are still out there about whether or not alcohol is safe during pregnancy.

So tell me, Gina, a little bit about your work with the University of Anchorage, Alaska and are you able to bring the FASD into that work at all?

Gina: Yes, actually. They wanted someone impacted (by a disability). I had a friend help me with my resume; I had never written one before. I've never needed references before, and I have never done an interview. I wasn't sure how that was going to go. The University (UAA) wanted someone impacted and wanted someone with lived experience. I got the job and work two days a week right now. I'm helping them create a survey of people with disabilities, bringing in the perspective of someone who is differently abled. They want me to verify that the language is simple and straightforward, that it's not too long, and that the questions are self-explanatory. The University wants to know why more people with disabilities don't apply for the health field in their college. There are so many people with disabilities out there now. Putting all disabilities together, I believe it's one in four people is disabled in some manner. That's a big, untapped pool of people that don't apply for a variety of different reasons. Is it a question of whether accommodations are available? Is it low self-esteem? Stigma? Not wanting the school or employers to know about disability status?

Patti: So, are you interacting with students coming in? Or are you only helping out with the creation of this process?

Gina: I'm helping with the creation of the survey, and when it is ready, we will market it to potential students online.

Patti: So, Gina, is there anything that you would hope that readers might be able to join or partner with you on anything that you're doing?

Gina: I think it would be neat to get more adults on board and supporting each other and collaborating on projects. I think that with some good content, I think it would be really good to have that. "Flying with Broken Wings" is a wonderful site on Facebook for adults with FASD as well as caregivers for those with FASD. I'm a moderator on there. We've got 6.4 thousand members in that group. You will absolutely love it, Patti, if you join our community. You're going to thank me forever for this because it's a great site. I've been on it for years. Sometimes it gets a little touchy because we want everybody to feel included in it, but sometimes caregivers don't like hearing our complaints. They find it overwhelming sometimes. But, I mean, you have to take the good with the bad.

Patti: It's all part of life. Because as much as we can scare them with our experiences, we can also offer them hope the way no one else can.

Gina: Absolutely.

Patti: I've walked that line, so to speak, in the type one diabetes world. Families of kids with FASD tend to be very isolated, these parents feel judged by everyone for the behavior of their child because everyone views behavior as a matter of choice and not realizing that FASD is a physical disability, especially if their child has not yet been diagnosed.

Gina: And so a lot of these rooms tend to be places where it's just vent, vent, vent. But this is a good group.

Patti: With diabetes, when a new person joins (the group) because their kiddo was just diagnosed, there's an outpouring of sympathy. "Oh, I'm so sorry for you." That drives me nuts! I don't know any other way of life; Diabetes is all I've ever known. I wouldn't be who I am without type one diabetes. It's given me the strength of character that I would not have had otherwise. And definitely resilience. It's the same with FASD; we may have a variety of impairments, but we have wonderful strengths that are underappreciated because people are so focused on deficits. We've got to get better at navigating the fine line between being deficit-based and strength-based. Gina, this conversation has been so delightful!

Gina: Thank you. It's been my pleasure. I feel like I just had coffee with a friend!

Searching for Biological Roots leads to a Diagnosis with FAS.

A Conversation with Rebecca Tillou

In this conversation, I speak with Rebecca Tillou, from New York, who is currently planning her third annual 5K Run fundraiser to benefit FASD United. To participate in these annual Run FASD events, please refer to the information in the Appendix. She is the author of *Tenacity* and is a member of FASCETS (Fetal Alcohol Spectrum Consultation, Education and Training Services) Board of Directors.

Patti: Hi Rebecca. Thank you for taking the time to meet with me. I thought we could sit down and talk about our journeys, figuring out as adults that we have been impacted by fetal alcohol spectrum disorder. That's a big shift that each of us went through.

Rebecca: Yeah.

Patti: Yeah. So if you could just share a little bit about your journey and what led you to that discovery?

Rebecca: Absolutely. I am 43 years old. I was adopted as an infant out of New Jersey when I was one month old. The doctors told my parents I was a healthy baby girl with no complications. At the time of my adoption, New Jersey's adoptions were closed or sealed. Not anymore, but they were back in the 80s. So my parents took everything that the doctor said at face value and took me home. Once I was home is when I started to get really sick. I had ear infections and bronchitis constantly. I had failure to thrive, meaning I was not meeting height and weight requirements as I should have been. I also wasn't eating normally, even bottle feedings, for 18 months, and my parents didn't know why. So they took me to John Hopkins and had me tested for every genetic issue doctors could think of, and everything came back normal.

My pediatrician had mentioned Fetal Alcohol Syndrome to my parents. As it was known back in 1980, the pediatrician said that I had the facial features, which were wide-set eyes and smooth philtrum, or the space between the upper lip and the nose. He wondered if my not eating might be a result of FAS. But then, when my parents got tubes in my ears at eighteen months because of my chronic ear infections, everything started to normalize. I started to eat. I started to gain weight, and all my milestones were met on time. So the diagnosis of FAS was never made.

So, I was a good student from kindergarten through senior year, but it was a very structured learning environment in which I thrived. My parents created a structured home environment, and it was not overwhelming. My parents used lots of visuals because it was how they operated, but just because they didn't know that I was neurodivergent at the time. But that's how they lived their life, and it worked. So, I made it through elementary, junior high, and high school with success.

I started to fall apart, though, in college when I had to go out on my own. I majored in speech therapy to be a speech therapist. One of my assignments was to student teach at actual residences. I had to come up with lesson plans on my own. I thought they made sense. The professors disagreed and said my work was "all over the place." I graduated with an undergraduate degree in Communicative Sciences and Disorders and went on to graduate school. They had me tested for a learning disability in graduate school because my lesson plans were not up to par, and the result was simply "Executive functioning deficits." I was not fit to write diagnostic reports and in-linked reports. None of us realized at the time that my birth mother had drunk during her pregnancy. So the faculty at my graduate school just said I had issues with executive functioning because that's all that they had figured out. I failed to graduate from school because I could not meet their standards of writing and teaching students.

I got married in 2004. I have two kids, and I work full-time as an insurance representative for medical claims for a car insurance company. So, for people that are injured in car accidents, I take care of their claims. I'm still doing the same job fifteen years later. I am very good at it because it's very redundant and it's very structured. That's what my brain needs; that's how I learn, and I've been successful.

So when I was 34 years old, I went to see my parents in South Carolina with my two-year-old little guy. Right after we got home to New York, my mom received a pamphlet in the mail from the adoption agency that had placed me. The agency sends out pamphlets every so often. My mom picked it up, and it had a section on Fetal Alcohol Spectrum Disorders or FASD.

She put it aside, picked it up the next day, and flipped through it. My mom and I have always gotten along, but sometimes we feel like ships passing in the night. We would try to shop together and cook together, but it never lasted. I would become frustrated or disinterested. Now, she and I have had a tough relationship. We just never really clicked. In some ways, yes, but not in others, and we just wondered why and thought it was different genetics. You know, you click with some, you don't with others. So, she read this pamphlet. By then, I had found my birth family. I knew my birth mother was a chronic alcoholic, and she had drank through her entire pregnancy with me. So because I had told my mom all of this, and after she read the pamphlet, she called me on the phone, and she's, I mean, I could hear it in her voice that she was crying. She said, "I want to read this to you. I think you might have a Fetal Alcohol Spectrum Disorder." She listed off symptoms: trouble with impulsivity, trouble with math, time management, and social situations - those are all struggles for me. Yeah. So by the time she finished reading it all off to me, we were both crying. So then I decided I was going to pursue a diagnosis. At 34 years old, I had no idea where to go (to get diagnosed). At that point, there was not a lot out there. There's still not a lot more than there was nine or ten years ago, but it's still scarce compared to some other disabilities that are also invisible.

Patti: We have our work cut out for us.

Rebecca: And we will change the world. We will not give up until we are heard. So I decided to get diagnosed. There are really no diagnosticians in Albany, New York, who diagnose adults. There is nobody. So I reached out to a pediatrician, a geneticist, actually, and I told her my story. I sent in photos of me as a baby that showed I had the facial features of Fetal Alcohol Syndrome. The geneticist took my case even though she only treats children. Yeah, she took me on.

She diagnosed me with Fetal Alcohol Syndrome, FAS, which is under the umbrella of Fetal Alcohol Spectrum Disorders, FASD. I have FAS because, as a baby, I had facial features that have dissipated over time. I also have a small head, social issues, and other characteristics that you can't really see. I told the geneticist about all of it. I told her my birth mother drank. She asked if I had ever talked to my birth mom, and I said no, she died before I found her, like in 1999, of an alcohol-related death. She asked how I knew that. I said from talking with people she worked with and knew her well. They told me they always saw her drunk, and one of them said that she was drunk when she went into labor and up until she went to the hospital to have me. So that's where my story for advocacy for FASD started.

Patti: One element of your story is a shortcoming in the diagnostic process, I think: the reliance on written documentation of maternal drinking.

Rebecca: Exactly.

Patti: Documentation is almost impossible to get, especially for children in the foster care system, because hospitals don't routinely test for alcohol. They only test for drugs, which is done by a far less expensive screening tool. Testing for alcohol is expensive, so it's not typically done, aside from the consideration that alcohol is legal. But without that written documentation, nobody wants to diagnose the children that I've been working with for the last twenty-two years.

Rebecca: No.

Patti: Even though alcohol affects our brains so much more invasively and is so much more dangerous than "street drugs" because alcohol molecules are so much smaller than the molecules for those others. Because of the molecule's small size, it gets into structures that other drugs don't. Alcohol is also classified as a neurotoxin because it dissolves the myelin sheath of brain cells.

Rebecca: It does. In closed adoptions, like mine, little information is available. Some doctors want verbal confirmation from the birth mother. That's just not needed. If you want to help us, you've got to let that go.

Patti: Verbal confirmation is the only thing I have. I have not been formally diagnosed. I found out five years ago, when I was fifty-four when I asked my mother if she drank when she carried me. She answered, "Oh, yeah, every day." That was normal in the '50s and '60s. Because my "quirks" lined up with everything I was learning about FASD, I don't need more confirmation than that. Then everything made sense. Suddenly, there were so many shifts in the way I understood all my quirks.

So it took me a while to process the idea of sharing this information. When I finally said something to my supervisor, she was like, "Oh, well, that doesn't surprise me." What? Wow. Apparently, some of my quirks were, you know, louder than I realized, and people around me just would just say, "Oh, that's just Patti."

Rebecca: That's how everyone referred to me, "That's just Rebecca."

Patti: Thank you for sharing your story with me. Speaking of stories, your book is fantastic.

Rebecca: Thank you.

Patti: I absolutely loved it. I had a hard time putting it down. This past week, I've been writing a foster care home study, and I was really torn about writing that vs. reading your book. Your book won.

Rebecca: Thank you.

Patti: It is such a beautiful adoption journey and journey of searching. You so beautifully conveyed the highs and the lows and the frustrations, the acceptance, and the peace that you've found by the end. I loved all the nuances in how your other relationships have been strengthened in some ways and challenged in others.

Rebecca: And the healing that's come everywhere.

Patti: Yeah. I really like how you tied in some of the FASD hints throughout your journey. And then at the end of the book, explaining it all, giving the reader a FASD lesson. So many things I was really relating to.

Rebecca: I'm so glad.

Patti: I laughed out loud when you were talking about visiting that pediatric geneticist, at your description of being, you know, in your thirties and following the little colored footsteps down the hall. It was as if I was with you as you walked down the hallway. But I was also kind of tripping out at what the doctor focused on in her physical examination. So tell me about the lines, or creases, on your hands because I had never heard that before.

Rebecca: So this is crazy. Nobody uses that anymore, apparently. It is a physical sign that is not used anymore, but she did. It's called a hockey stick formation. It's on the palms of your hand, and it looks like a hockey stick from the index finger down to under the pinky finger.

Patti: (stares at hands)

Rebecca: My mom has the hockey sticks too, and my grandmother didn't drink. So she's not on the spectrum. But I'm also told some children with Down syndrome have it, too, so this is why nobody uses that physical sign anymore.

Patti: Yes, just as the number of "abnormal" facial signs has changed over time. There used to be a lot of characteristics, and now it's just the three.

Rebecca: Yes. The eyes, or shortened palpebral fissures, the smooth area between the lip and the nose, or philtrum, and the super thin upper lip.

Patti: I don't think I had those signs as a kid. But I do have small eye openings. Before I had my cataracts out, they used a machine to measure the shape of your eyeball in order to determine the prescription built into the new lens for your distance. So, in theory, after you have your cataract removed and new lenses put in, you don't need to wear glasses.

Rebecca: Right.

Patti: Because your distance is taken care of, except my eye openings are small enough that the guy kept saying, "Open wider, open wider." So I'm like this. (Stretches eyes wide open) And now I only have 20/20 vision if I do this (Stretches eyes wide open again). Let me ask you, how far can you drive with your eyes open this wide? (Still opening eyes wide) So, I'm still wearing glasses.

Rebecca: Eyes as an indicator of FAS can be tricky. Because the fissures, or openings, are small, the eyes look far apart, but they're really not, although I have seen a few with FASD whose eyes truly are set far apart. That's just not typical.

Patti: After I figured out that I am on the spectrum when I was at the optometrist's office for grins and giggles, I asked her if I have small eye openings. She said yes. I think this is the only physical sign, at least on my face, that I have of FASD. So the other thing that you noted in your book about physical characteristics was something about your pinky toes.

Rebecca: Yep.

Patti: I really resonated with that, and I'll tell you why after you explain it.

Rebecca: So I have weird feet. They're extremely narrow and my pinky toes don't have regular toenails. One of them has never had a nail. And the other one? It grows, but it grows weirdly. Seriously, it looks like a booger. Like it looks like a hard booger, it's so gross. And I just like to clip it from the top.

Patti: So the nail does not lay flat on your toe?

Rebecca: So every once in a while, and I just cut the top off. It's weird. There's a name for it, actually. It's called hypoplasia of the toenails. It isn't necessarily, but it can be indicative of an FASD because the alcohol affects whatever happens to be developing at the time of exposure.

Patti: And that's what a lot of people don't realize. They just think it is a developmental disorder, failing to realize that it affects not just our brains but everything. So, all of our being. So the reason I resonated with this bit in your book about piggy toes is that this is just one more oddity that got reshuffled when I learned about it possibly being caused by alcohol exposure. My pinky toes are so short they don't even make it up to the knuckle of the fourth toe. Both toes have nails, but the nails don't touch the skin. They go out at a 45-degree angle, like your nail.

Rebecca: That's funny. I don't know why they do that. Something with the alcohol when the nail was initially forming. People think I think I'm crazy (to talk about little things like this), but I want people to know that there are so many intricacies. Not everyone gets weird things like this. It's like they say, "If you meet one person with an FASD, you've met one person."

Patti: I'm caring for my mother, who has Lewy Body Dementia, and we have that same saying in that circle too. No two people are alike. No matter what our medical or developmental, or psychological condition, we all have unique bodies, brains, and experiences. Lewy Body is the second most common form of dementia, though hardly anyone has heard of it, even in medical circles. Just as with Lewy Body, the prevalence of FASD is hugely unrecognized. With FASD, it is 2.5 times more prevalent than Autism Spectrum Disorders, yet hardly anyone can tell you what it is. There's such a high percentage of people living with it who don't get proper support, who struggle with anxiety and depression, and may eventually choose to take their own life. Early identification and intervention makes a world of difference and can prevent the horribly negative outcomes that scare every parent who ever searches FASD on the internet to see what it is. It's 5% - that's one in every twenty people! But most of us are mis- or undiagnosed, in large part due to the misinformation and stigma associated with it. How many of us are told we don't have it because we "don't have the face" or because we're "not retarded." If you and I had known earlier in life and had the proper context for our "quirks," what might be different for us?

Rebecca: I appreciate them (quirks) more than my husband does. My kids find them very humorous, though.

Patti: Have you looked at the study by Myles Himmelreich, C.J. Lutke, and Emily Travis Hargrove?

Rebecca: They're with The Changemakers. Yes.

Patti: They did a study on all the co-morbid conditions that are often present in those with FASDs.

Rebecca: I know they did. I met C.J. I met her in DC.

Patti: I listened to them present on one of my favorite FASD podcasts, FASD Family Life. I had to listen to it five times because it was so impactful. So FASD is also present alongside many autoimmune disorders. I had a couple of neurobehavioral trainers tell me that alcohol exposure was probably the cause of my type 1 diabetes. So when I met Dr. Kenneth Jones, who discovered FAS, I asked him about that, and he assured me it was not a causal relationship. Their survey (Himmelreich, Lutke, and Hargrove) compared the prevalence of hundreds of conditions within those with FASD who completed their lengthy questionnaire with the prevalence of those same conditions in the general population. The findings are staggering and point to a tremendous need for more research into FASD as a whole-body diagnosis.

Rebecca: Yeah, they're amazing researchers. They're young.

Patti: I'm scanning down their research paper as we talk. Significantly high rates of cleft palate. We're far more likely to have a low weight.

Rebecca: Which I was when I was little.

Patti: I was always the shortest or next to the shortest kid in my grade, but I was not underweight. Oh, when I was studying the neurobehavioral model, they mentioned the effects of alcohol on teeth. We are more likely to need orthodontia.

Rebecca: Yes, which I did.

Patti: So did I.

Rebecca: I still have issues with my teeth. As a child, I will tell you, I thought it was normal. Apparently, it's not; but I thought it was normal to go to the dentist and have teeth pulled at every appointment. Just one at a time because my mouth was so small, they had to make room for my adult teeth. I thought that was normal. My mouth is still so small that I use a child-sized toothbrush.

Patti: When I was in fifth grade, they pulled 11 teeth at once so that my adult teeth would grow in at the right time for braces. But it's not just that – alcohol exposure can interfere with enamel formation.

Rebecca: Yes, I was blessed with really strong teeth. And that is really a genetic trait on my mom's side. Because when I met my biological uncle, that was the first thing he told me.

Patti: I read that in your book. But you know, I think of all the kids that have been on my caseload through the decades that had a mouthful of silver. There's an expression in foster care about "bottle rot," but it's not that at all; it's the absence of enamel on a prenatally exposed child that leaves teeth susceptible to rot and decay. Without enamel, even a Keto diet will rot your teeth. I also learned in my training that you can have too few teeth or too many teeth. So here's the weird thing, I am missing four molars. And my maternal uncle had four extra.

Rebecca: Well, he stole them.

Patti: That's what I always used to joke. But learning this made me wonder about my grandmother.

Rebecca: Oh, my goodness. And it's usually. And now it goes down the line. Like my grandmother was an alcoholic. I think my birth mom had an FASD. Oh, yeah. And gut issues are extremely common. For instance, not to talk about poop, but I always thought it was normal not to go more than once every four or five days! No joke, I only realized that's not normal three years ago. And then I was like, oh, wait. It's all connected. It's because of alcohol exposure.

Patti: Yeah. It's easy to quickly say that not everything is alcohol exposure. And yes, that's true. Too few in the medical field consider that alcohol exposure needs to be one of the many explanations for various physical signs and symptoms when they are making diagnoses.

Rebecca: It boggles my mind that doctors, nurses, and midwives still say, oh, you can have a glass of red wine (when you're pregnant). I don't know why they say that; I don't get it! I don't understand why they'll say no to drug use, but you can drink. Like, of all people that should know, I don't understand.

Patti: Thirty years after starting my career in the drug & alcohol field, I'm learning about what alcohol does to the brain and what it does to preborn babies.

So with this new awareness, you felt led to write your book, your beautiful adoption and searching story that also educates readers about FASDs. What else are you now doing?

Rebecca: I have become a self-advocate as well as an advocate for those affected in some way by FASD. Whether it be the parents, the guardians, or the people themselves, I actually began an annual 5K two years ago in 2021 to raise awareness for FASD. 2023 This will be the third year. It's held every September as part of International FASD Awareness Month, and it benefits FASD United. Every year we try to do it a little bigger, get a little more awareness out there. We're trying to get some big sponsors, which is tough. It's tough because nobody understands it. During COVID, I started running further and further and further because I needed something to get out of the house. That's what led to me wanting to do a fundraiser with running. And my mom actually suggested doing it for FASD. Then my husband coined the term Run FASD, which is a great pun on the run fast. When I was a guest on Natalie Vecchione's podcast, FASD Hope, she asked me, "Where do you see yourself five years from now?" I think that was in 2021. And I was like, "Well, I want to do a fundraiser for FASD. I want to do a run." She's like, "Okay, let's do it!" So we got Jen Wisdahl from FASD United to join forces, and this year will be the third fundraiser.

Patti: I think I've heard you on both Robbie's and Natalie's podcast.

Rebecca: So that's my baby. And I never thought it would come to fruition. We put it together in, I think, three or four months the first year, and we had a good turnout. All proceeds go to FASD United.

Patti: So tell me about the growth in the run from year to year.

Rebecca: So the first year, I'm not going to get the numbers right. But the first year, we did the US, and we did Canada. We can't go into the UK and stuff because there's something with taxes and money. There's something that prevents us right now from going into the UK that won't allow us to send the bling like the medals or the shirts over there right now. They could still hold the event and donate but without the goodies. So the first year, I think it raised, I might be wrong with this, six or seven thousand dollars; we only had a few sponsors. This past September, we had so many more sponsors. And I think we ended up raising… I want to say it was roughly $15,000.

Patti: But money for FASD United is only half of your goal.

Rebecca: That's right. Growing awareness is just as important. So this past year, what we did differently was that we had people do meet-up groups within their communities. I didn't want to worry about it. For example, I live in a small town in New York, and we had a group of 15 people. This coming September, I would love to have 50 or 75. Each year it's getting bigger and more awareness is raised. This past year was still small, mostly other parents with FASD, so there's still a lot of work to be done. We're getting there. Thanks to promoting it on podcasts and in social media, it is gaining momentum all over the country. Florida had five runs. There are kids that rode bikes. So you can bike. You can walk. You can run. You can do whatever you want. It's to raise awareness of FASD and to raise funds for the non-profit FASD United.

Patti: I know I advertised for you all over my pages.

Rebecca: Thank you. So in California, were there community runs there too?

Patti: I believe there were several (communities) that did, but I'm not sure where. I will, of course, be promoting Run FASD again this year!

Rebecca: I don't remember what I was going to say. That's something else with FASD. Word retrieval and memory can go. Some days we're spot on. But lately, not. I think I have a lot going on, like (parenting) busy kids.

Patti: So FASD can interfere with memory in a lot of ways, like storing information in memory banks.

Rebecca: Yes.

Patti: A lot of us have trouble sleeping, which is when stuff goes from short-term to long-term memory.

Rebecca: Right.

Patti: And so retrieving information can be impacted too.

Rebecca: Yeah. I require at least 10 hours of sleep to feel really awake during the day. I was always the last kid to wake up at sleepovers. I always thought it was just me, but now I know it's the FAS. Everyone laughs at me because I require a lot of sleep. But it's my brain.

Patti: Nobody realizes how much harder our brains work than brains that have not been compromised by alcohol exposure, drug exposure, or by trauma.

Rebecca: They work so much harder. I don't even want to put a number on it compared to average people's brains. It can be exhausting.

Patti: That's a huge thing that foster parents complain about. Because when kids are exhausted, they're cranky.

Rebecca: Right.

Patti: A lot of these kids, I mean, they're just really, really cranky because they're mentally exhausted. Plus, you throw a trauma in there, and everyone in the home is triggered. So if you've been physically abused and you've trained yourself to sleep with one eye open, then not much information goes from short-term to long-term storage and consequently gets lost.

Rebecca: This leads to academic struggles in school.

Patti: Yes, It's all connected. I've been working with two local foster family agencies to train them in FASCETS Neurobehavioral Model, which is a wonderful organization that really looks at how, in today's language, FASD is a physical disability with behavioral symptoms.

Rebecca: Right.

Patti: It is a physical change in our brain that affects every part of us. Therefore, it is technically a physical disability. But the neurobehavioral model really emphasizes building on strengths in coming up with accommodations tailored to each person's struggles. And FASCETS is so right – those with invisible disabilities are equally as deserving of accommodations as are people whose disabilities happen to be visible.

Rebecca: Absolutely. You know it's ethical, but it's so hard if you don't have the facial feature changes. Very few people on the spectrum have those facial feature changes. It's between five to seven percent of those on the spectrum, I think.

Patti: I've read anywhere from one to ten percent. Facial changes only occur if alcohol exposure occurs between days 17 and 21 of pregnancy. Who even knows they are pregnant at that point? So in your case, you had those physical signs as an infant, but over time, your facial structure changed, as happens with all of us.

Rebecca: Yeah.

Patti: So, you know, I'm passionate about reaching the child welfare, at least in my area.

Rebecca: Absolutely.

Patti: And getting local mental health to start working with the developmental agencies because right now, those two systems of care are pointing the finger at each other. Mental Health says, "FASD, that's a developmental thing. Go over to the regional center." And the developmental agency says, "Oh, no, it's a behavioral thing. Go back to mental health." And so nobody is helping these children.

Rebecca: Which is crazy because when I was a speech therapist for a few years, we worked together. A speech therapist works with OT and PT. So, but that's all physical.

Patti: So, on the physical side, they all work nicely together. So why can't mental health work with the developmental agencies? I sometimes wonder if the barrier is wanting to avoid the financial costs of providing assistance, but then I remind myself that these systems are refusing to look at just how mammoth a problem FASD really is. They want to believe very few people have FASD when in reality, it affects 5% of the general population. I really don't care who has "responsibility" for FASD on a fiscal basis. I just want to give better tools to everybody that supports these children and adults who have FASD as well!

Rebecca: I know. But it's also the stigma, which is another huge issue. The stigma that the birth mom drank.

Patti: 45% of pregnancies are unplanned.

Rebecca: Exactly. And roughly seven percent of women don't find out the pregnant until they're six weeks along. So they could have been drinking that whole time. And that's not their fault.

34

nd one of one of the detours in my college years was to attend
ıg school, which I didn't finish. But I'll never forget what they said in
ıernity rotation: that one-third of women continue having periods for the
ırst three months of pregnancy. So, if you're still having your period, why
would you stop drinking?

Rebecca: Exactly. So I don't know how to break the stigma against women
except by raising awareness that we can't blame women for doing
something when they didn't even know they were pregnant. Raising
awareness is so critical! So many of us are doing what we can! The big thing
out there right now is the FASD Respect Act – this has huge implications at
the University level – to ensure funding so that future educators and doctors
and nurses and social workers, and therapists get educated about FASD.
And it almost passed this year.

Patti: I know. I was brokenhearted to find out it failed by one vote.

Rebecca: Many of us were brokenhearted, but that just means we have to
work harder now in 2023. It just wasn't time. I mean, it's overdue. But we'll
do it this year. We just have to start over. And give them the money numbers
– what does FASD cost the nation without support, how much adequate
interventions would cost, and how much savings would there be by
addressing it vs. continuing to sweep it under the rug?

Patti: And that's huge. It would be so much easier if we didn't have to
educate the masses and get them to view behavior as a reflection of brain
function rather than of intentional choices.

Rebecca: I know.

Patti: I like one of the key phrases from FASCETS, and I use it all the time:
None of us knew what we didn't know until we learned it."

Rebecca: Exactly.

Patti: They don't teach this stuff in grad school. I never learned any alternative to behavior equals intentional choices. It's out-of-the-box thinking.

Rebecca: Yeah. And they don't want to go out of the box. A lot of people are older, and there's like a lot of the older educators are stuck in the old ways. Yeah. Trying to change anything within academia is a nightmare, Just like trying to change anything in the government. I know. But, you know, a big part of the struggle is their ignorance.

Patti: Yes, it's not that the people that taught us were trying to mislead us. They're just sincerely wrong. Neuroscience has only been solidifying what we know about brain function for the last 20 years.

Rebecca: The neurologist I went to go see didn't know much about FASD, and somebody else I know had a very similar experience. Doctors just don't seem to know much about FASD, which is shocking because it's so prevalent. The neurologist I saw said to me at the beginning of the appointment, "I googled FASD right before I saw you. You don't have facial features. That's all I know." And I'm like, "You're a brain doctor. I don't understand." But that's not what they focus on.

Patti: Same with Type 1 Diabetes; it has a lot of things in common with Type 2, but treatment is very different because the processes that underlie the development of symptoms are so very different. That isn't covered adequately in med schools or in nursing schools. You get a lecture for thirty minutes. So with FASD, it's not covered in social work or psychology, not even in grad school. They also don't teach adoption issues in social work schools. Social work school is all about theory. Systems theory is good, none of us is an island to ourselves, but we need to learn application also. Adoption issues are huge – it's a very complex dynamic. Possibly because if they taught it and all the struggles that go with child welfare, nobody would want to be in that field. 80% of children with FASD end up not being raised by their parents. They are raised by relatives or within foster care. But since 86% of them were either not diagnosed, or mis-diagnosed, their needs went unidentified, and unsupported. Their caregivers were not taught how to meet their needs, and these youth are far more likely than most in the foster care system to wind up bouncing around from home to home to home. Social workers and therapists who assume behavior is intentional tend to get cynical about these kids' prognosis and are frustrated by all the "extra work" they create by their "intentional behavior." It is heartbreaking all around, from every perspective!

Rebecca: My adoptive family was wonderful, and I was never "in the system," but I've heard horribly sad stories.

Patti: To last long as a professional within child welfare, it's a calling. If you're not called to it, you won't last, just like with my other job, with hospice. It's a calling. With so many specialized bodies of knowledge, you have to seek it out. And unless you have a reason to seek out FASD, who's going to do that?

Rebecca: Right.

Patti: You'll seek out things that seem more pertinent to whatever your field is.

Rebecca: Yeah. I have a psychologist friend whom I ate breakfast with a few weeks ago. We were talking about FASD. She's my age, so she's been out of college for a while. She said when she was in college, "They covered FASD. I think in one sentence." I was dumbfounded.

Patti: With my business, one of the main things I focus on is coaching parents. I have a four-month coaching program that's based upon what I learned at FASCETS, but I throw in other things I've learned in practice that are so critical, such as adoption issues, trauma, attachment, and the intergenerational nature of so much of that. I also have a four-month program for adults. I started that to meet the needs of a fellow coach, and got hooked on helping adults transform the way they see themselves. I want to reach people like us who have always felt themselves to be a little bit different. Not quite fitting in, not understanding perhaps why they struggled in life. Maybe, like you, they were adopted but never got the opportunity to learn of their birth family history, as you did. Perhaps the families they grew

37

up with were chaotic, and they buried their years of rejection, fear, pain, or trauma in drugs or alcohol but never realized what was underneath the surface.

Rebecca: Depending on how deeply we've been impacted, that could be huge!

Patti: So if they read or hear what they have in common with everyone who participates in this project, they may be inspired to explore FASD further as an explanation for so much in life.

Rebecca: Exactly. I think it's important that people recognize that FASD is a big thing. People tend to think of it as a childhood issue.

Patti: I know without stopping to think that those kids turn eighteen or twenty-one, and the challenges are still there, even though services really aren't. Services are hard to find, anyway. Nobody realizes that one of the primary effects of FASD is dysmaturity, in other words, our social and emotional development is at a much slower pace than our physical development. For so many, our social and emotional development is years younger than our chronological age, sometimes by half. This is why it floors me that at eighteen, you age out of foster care. When a significant percentage of kids in foster care have an FASD, there are insufficient resources to ensure they can live independently when many have a significantly younger developmental age than their chronological age. Another frustration I dealt with chronically is that in foster care preservice training, people are told kids in care are often half of their age, but not any of the implications of that truth.

Rebecca: Really?

Patti: Yes. Perspective foster or resource parents are told that the children who are going to be placed in your home are going to be about half their age emotionally and socially. But they stopped there. Nothing further about how to work with a child who is that much younger on the inside. They don't think about prompting parents to help their children with tasks as if they were at a younger age. They never think about what age the kids will be emotionally and socially when they emancipate. And yet we wonder why the outcomes are so poor for so many youths. Foster care is a necessary evil that, paradoxically, I have been blessed to be part of for more than twenty years. While children are safer physically because they're not understood, and because this leads to so many transitions between homes, they get traumatized again and again due to attachment disruptions. Foster care both blesses and damages many children.

Rebecca: Doesn't foster care extend to twenty-one now?

Patti: Yes, in most states. The company I worked for almost twenty-two years had a transitional age youth program. It stayed full and always had a waiting list. While I never worked in that program, I did manage on-call for them on a rotating basis. Many of the calls from those young adults were calls you would expect from an eight, nine or ten-year-old in terms of their problem-solving skills. It was frustrating to get a call in the middle of the night, well after curfew, from someone who forgot their apartment key or who wanted a ride home. But, knowing that so many foster youth have an FASD and, therefore, a great many suffer dysmaturity... that fits.

Rebecca: Absolutely.

Patti: Because the system itself is traumatizing. You can't remove someone from their family without it being traumatic and put them in the home of strangers. That's traumatic. It may be far safer, but it's still traumatic.

Rebecca: Exactly. It's scary! Of course, I remember nothing from when I was one month old.

Patti: My heart breaks for these kids. It breaks for these young adults. It breaks for the foster parents, the resource parents who are expected to care for them without being given enough information and without getting adequate training. They get what feels like tons of training, but that's because they get a lot within a very short period of time. They're flooded with information and forget most of it before they even complete the training process. I think training on FASD and how alcohol, drugs, and trauma change the brain needs to be mandatory.

Rebecca: Yes, in all 50 states. And really, in Canada as well. I feel like there are (some provinces in Canada) light years ahead of us, but they feel like we're light years ahead of them.

Patti: I understand that there is at least one province, though I don't know which one, which has an entire school district for FASD.

Rebecca: Wow.

Patti: This brings up another critical piece: it seems we need to be fluent in two languages: one that is disability and deficit-focused and the other which is difference-focused and more strength-based.

Rebecca: And working to educate people to transition from being deficit focused to strength focused.

Patti: Exactly. In order for someone to thrive, you have to identify strengths and highlight them and use them in setting up accommodations, which is just a fancy word for a workaround for those things that are challenging.

Rebecca: Like list making, using apps on your phone, like the calendar and the notepad features.

Patti: Yes, exactly. One of the goals we must adopt is shifting the way our society views things from being deficit-minded to being strength-based and normalizing neurodiversity - everybody is different. It's hard because if we put too much emphasis on the strength-based, then we won't get services. As our structures are now, nobody's going to fund services for people that have all these strengths.

Rebecca: I know.

Patti: But if we put too much emphasis on the deficit side of things, then what harm do we do to somebody's psyche?

Rebecca: I know. It's a Catch-22. I feel like I've been lucky in that I am a successful human. I now have a husband and kids and a full-time job, while many of us with FASD struggle with that. The "disability" label doesn't feel right to me because I am highly functioning.

Patti: That's the tough reality of spectrum disorders. Folks like you and I are on the higher end of the spectrum. We're smart, but that doesn't mean that our judgment was always good, especially in the coming-of-age years, when some of our bad decisions were truthfully outright dangerous. We lacked the insight to know better, despite being smart. Then that brings in the shame. But for many, the challenges are far more pervasive, leaving a great many incapable of ever being independent.

Rebecca: Yeah. But everyone has strengths, and we need to speak to those strengths. Somehow, we need to get the strengths to tie in through the struggling side, and it just... people just need to hear us out. Strengths build self-confidence; if you don't have self-confidence, you got nothing.

Patti: So what was it like processing the discovery of having FASD? Did all of a sudden, things make sense in a different way? What was that like for you?

Rebecca: I was so excited because I was able to look back in life and be like, "Oh, my gosh!" Well, this is why I struggled in math. Or this is why I didn't always think before I would do things. Everything made sense suddenly. And I like that. I had a reason for why some things are still really hard, like with money issues. Now it makes sense. It's why I don't go Christmas shopping on my own anymore -- because I don't have a good concept of money. I have a concept of it, but not a great one. Instead, I focus on the joy that I'll get by giving everyone their gifts, absolutely. But I can't track all the prices in my head. So then, when I get up to the register, I'm like, "Oh!" But everything all of a sudden made sense, and everything fell in place. Yeah, and my mom felt the same way; she now realizes my brain works differently. The greatest part of this discovery is that my relationship with my mom is so much stronger now.

Patti: Yay!

Rebecca: My birthday was a couple of days ago, and today I got a package from my mom. She sent me a piece of jewelry that she had made that says "tenacious" on it. Yeah. My book is Tenacity, and my spirit is so tenacious. I think of the fights my mom and I used to have… it was my brain just not really comprehending things she was saying before I spoke. We both have Italian tempers, too, so that didn't help. So understanding my brain works differently has helped me and both my parents. My husband originally asked me why I wanted to get diagnosed because it wouldn't change anything. I said it might answer questions and make me understand myself better. We've had some issues during this journey of finding my birth mother and seeking my FASD diagnosis formally. Knowing doesn't make things right, but it makes us both have an understanding, and it helps to replace frustration with compassion.

Patti: Some things feel hard to be compassionate about when our focus is on ourselves, but when you think of behavior not as something that has to change but as a symptom of a brain injury, it makes a difference in how we respond to one another. I think of all the struggles the kids on my caseload had – now I know that it was because of their exposure to alcohol. For instance, if we have trouble linking cause and effect, there's nothing to keep us from acting on our impulses.

Rebecca: Cause and effect is also tough. And it's probably the hardest thing to teach kids. All kids, but especially those who are neurodivergent because it's abstract. We have to do everything we can to make a difference.

Patti: Yes, we have to because FASD is conservatively 5% of the population, and that was before the COVID lockdowns when alcohol sales went up by 20%. The lockdowns may be over, but alcohol sales are still up by 20%.

Rebecca: We just have to get ahead of this thing, especially in schools.

Patti: Yes. Not just the teachers, but the administration, the behaviorists, the school psychologists, and social workers; they all need to understand this. They need to change the way that they interact with these kids. 5% -- that's one in every twenty kids. So guaranteed, there's a minimum of one kid in every classroom.

Rebecca: At a minimum. And that doesn't count the higher stats of kids in foster care and adoption, who, of course, are in those same classrooms.

Patti: Yes, child welfare and mental health need to get on board with this because the struggles that children in care have are so much greater than anyone would realize. Mental health sees aspects of FASD and provides diagnoses for these aspects, like ADHD, Reactive Attachment, Oppositional Defiant, Autism... But they miss the big picture – behavioral symptoms overlap between FASD and ALL these other diagnoses. Because children are tested for drugs but not alcohol, FASD goes unidentified. The systems of care want to blame the kids for their behavior, but these behaviors point to the mismatch between their abilities and the expectations people have for them.

Rebecca: Absolutely.

Patti: They are normal defensive behaviors. There are things that any of us do to protect ourselves from pain. We all get defensive and angry when we feel dismissed and rejected when no one seems to hear our cries for help. And when nobody understands our behavior because they do not realize we have some brain changes... then people with FASD get blamed, shamed, and punished for behavior that is biologically driven.

Rebecca: I know. They couldn't help it if they tried.

Patti: And when foster or resource parents are insufficiently trained, they don't recognize that the extremely obnoxious behaviors reflect extreme pain, and they get understandably overwhelmed. So they give a seven-day notice or a 14-day notice, and the kid is moved to another home that is just as ill-prepared, and on and on it goes. Children with FASD are far more likely to have multiple placement disruptions than neurotypical children. And each move disrupts their attachment system yet again, making it harder and harder for a child with FASD to form healthy relationships and also making them more and more vulnerable to those who would prey upon those who are starved for affection and approval. The social dangers get even bigger because kids with FASD are targets for bullies.

Rebecca: Yes. Kids can be cruel.

Patti: Yeah. I was bullied as a kid. At the time, I thought it was because I was the only diabetic in school. But that's one of those pieces that got reshuffled when I learned I'm on the FASD spectrum. It was my quirks that made me a target of bullying. Kids that befriended me generally lost all their other friends. But I remember one time I got invited to a sleepover at a cool girl's house. Of course, I said yes! But when I got there, they made me the guinea pig in their game of Truth or Dare. That's fairly mild.

Rebecca: But as kids get older, they can be preyed upon by all kinds of predators.

Patti: Especially if they're in foster care, where they are prime targets for CSEC (Commercial Sexual Exploitation of Children). Have you ever read The Accomplice? Highly educational but captivating because it is a biography of her family's journey, it truly is an excellent book, by Melissa Jacobus.

Rebecca: Oh, wow. Right.

Patti: And it's written by a mother and FASD advocate who shares her journey with her two kids who are impacted in different ways by FASD as they go through their transitional years. And it got ugly. Her daughter got sucked into the criminal justice system because she was used by criminals. And so, how many people in prison nationwide are there because they were preyed upon and they did not have the social prowess to read the danger cues. Even in adulthood, you can still be sucked in by someone who's very sophisticated in the way that they prey upon people.

Rebecca: I know. I was. I wrote about it in my book, Tenacity. So again, I come to realizations later in life of things that I went through and I come to terms with those events in their proper context. It takes me a while sometimes. When I was in high school, I dated a teacher who was also my track coach; he was twice my age. We had a relationship for a year and a half. He groomed me for it, but I didn't realize that until I saw a documentary on the exact same thing that I went through. It was of a teacher and a student. I was very naive. I was eighteen, and like we know, with dysmaturity, I was nine emotionally.

Patti: I totally understand. When I was freshly divorced from my first marriage, I was incredibly vulnerable. And even though I was a therapist, I got swept off my feet by a predator who tricked me into walking away from everything. House, career, pets. And it sucked up three years in my life. I still say that I'll be pleased to see him in heaven because that means he's repented, but I don't ever want to see him on earth again. It's still hard to wrap my brain around those years because it's a real challenge to accept that you can be that vulnerable, that gullible.

Rebecca: But, you know, I had, one way of dealing with it, by focusing on the positives. I met many incredible people at that time.

Patti: I did, too, that I never would have met otherwise.

Rebecca: Yeah. They helped me get out of that relationship, actually.

Patti: That's funny that you say that because that was part of my spiritual journey as well. We traveled quite a bit during that time, and in three years, I only remember buying insulin once. I think it's kind of like that biblical story of the widow who never ran out of oil. Yeah. I never ran out of insulin.

Rebecca: That's amazing. The group I joined were on my college campus, and some people saw them as a cult. They might have been, but they were there when I needed them, and they helped me. I keep in touch with very few of them now. They were a little much for me, but they helped me when I needed it. And for that, they were heaven-sent. I wrote a letter saying I wanted my family back, and I put in my Bible. I still have it. It was a few months after that when I went back to my family. But my mom prayed for a year and a half for me and went through hell with worry.

Patti: So did mine.

Rebecca: And I feel horrible. But my mom's like, "She'll come back in God's time." So it's another amazing thing that we have that in common

Patti: You know, it takes courage to be so transparent.

Rebecca: Yes. And I am transparent. I also feel like I have diarrhea of the mouth. That's another FASD thing. No boundaries.

Patti: Rebecca, thank you for sharing so much with me and with our readers!

Comorbid Conditions & Myth Busting
A Conversation with C.J. Lutke

In this conversation, I speak with Ms. C. J. Lutke, the youngest of three adopted children, all of whom have an FASD. CJ is a well-known FASD speaker and was part of a team of young adults providing FASD training to second-year medical students at the University of British Columbia. She sits on various committees, and is an FASD Mentor. She is a blogger. She is a founding member of the International Adult Leadership Collaborative of the FASD Changemakers. She was co-lead on the ALC's first Lay of the Land research survey and is the lead author of the second Lay of the Land Survey on the Quality of Life of Adults with FASD.

Patti: Thank you so much for joining me. First, let me say that I have admired you and two of your colleagues since I first heard you on Robbie Seale's podcast, FASD Family Life. I listened to it about five times because there was so much information in it. I really wanted to highlight what the three of you did to this audience because your work is too important to not be shouted from the mountaintops. So, I'm very glad you chose to participate in my book project. Can you talk a little bit about what got the three of you to do that research?

C.J.: It was at the Vancouver International FASD conference hosted by UBC (University of British Columbia). There were seven or eight of us at a dinner table when one of us mentioned he had to go in for a hernia repair. I mentioned I had a hernia repair, and then a couple of other people were like, "Oh yeah, I've had a hernia too." Then we started comparing medical histories. I was like, "Oh, I've had that," and "Oh, this happened to me." It was quite interesting. None of the people were genetically related, not geographically close, from all kinds of different backgrounds, different genders, different ages, and different ethnicities. Yet, we had very similar medical issues.

Patti: That kind of makes me wonder. So six years ago, I had major abdominal surgery with a vertical incision almost the entire length of my abdomen. Then three years ago, I went in for a hernia repair of what we thought were going to be two places along the incision. When I woke up, the surgeon said, "I gave you the deal of a lifetime. You paid for two repairs, but there were so many hernias in various states that I've rebuilt your abdominal wall."

C.J.: Oh gosh.

Patti: Yeah. It explained why recovery was so painful. Tell me, C.J., how did that dinner conversation turn into your research project? How did you go about designing that? How long did it take you guys from when the idea germinated till when you actually had survey questionnaires going out?

C.J.: The four of us who formed the International Adult Leadership Collaborative (ALC) of FASD Changemakers started asking everyone we knew what their histories included, and we compiled a very long list. Then we talked to doctors and researchers who specialize in FASD to see if they also noticed any of these patterns, and we found that two of them did have a couple of questions about this. So we spent a lot of time gathering all the information, developing the survey, and helping to find all the general population data for comparison. The work was done entirely by the ALC. My mother, who has been the manager of the ALC for 15 years, was Chair of the International FASD Research Conferences at the University of British Columbia (UBC) and arranged for UBC to facilitate the technical development of the survey through the use of their survey software and the launching of the survey via the UBC website. Because the Interprofessional Continuing Education department of UBC has hosted the premiere research conferences on FASD, their involvement in promoting our survey gave our project a lot of traction and credibility.

The response we got was not unexpected by the ALC, but all the "experts" said we would be unable to find the people we were looking for and because no one would want to fill out such a long survey. We proved them wrong on both counts by receiving more than 500 completed surveys back. That showed us how much people wanted to be heard and how much they wanted to contribute to the body of knowledge about FASD.

48

Patti: Yes. So most people don't think about FASD being a whole-body diagnosis.

C.J.: No, and I think, too, that there is some confusion about this survey, which was really about finding correlations.

Patti: Yes, correlational; these two things exist together in unusual frequency versus causality, where this caused that. Personally, I really don't need to know a cause for what led, for example, to my Type One Diabetes. It is an autoimmune disease, and your study notes that folks with FASD have a higher prevalence of autoimmune diseases. But that's not the important thing; taking care of it is.

C.J.: So, our project is not a study. It was a survey. That needs to be said because the studies are completely different and require ethics approval and things like that. However, our survey has since spawned multi-year studies funded by NIAAA at three sites: Vancouver, Seattle, and Atlanta. The numbers we used for general population prevalence were all well-vetted by experts prior to publication. Our purpose was not to be fear-mongering but rather to point out the significant higher occurrence rates within people with an FASD. There are other studies that sprang from the initial survey as well. The International ALC of the FASD Changemakers will launch yet another survey once their website is back up following some maintenance.

Patti: Pick one finding that was surprising to you.

C.J.: The early onset dementia one was quite surprising. Yeah. 206 times higher.

Patti: That made enough of an impact upon me, since my diabetes raises my risks for both Vascular Dementia and Alzheimer's, that I saw a neurologist and had baseline studies done, so I can track any decline and get support in place as soon as I need them.

C.J.: I was going to review the survey results last night in preparation for our call today, but I had a headache from a sinus infection. I'm better today.

Patti: You just triggered another memory. Do you know how the dentist will, at times, do a full pan x-ray where the camera moves around the circumference of your head? The last time I had one, the dentist said I had a sinus infection. I had no clue; I never felt a thing.

C.J.: I have a high pain tolerance too. We did ask about it on the survey, and that was like almost even for those who did vs. did not have a high pain tolerance. Yeah. That's a difficult thing to assess because it's so subjective. You know, I have a friend who said her pain tolerance was low, yet she had gone to the hospital for a frozen shoulder. She described her pain level as an "8" on that 1-10 scale. She was told, "No, that's more like an 11."

Patti: I've had frozen shoulder three times. It runs with diabetes. For me, it was more aggravating than painful. It was aggravating because it limited my ability to get things down from my cupboards. In fact, that's why I have short hair now: when I couldn't put it up in a ponytail anymore, I chopped it short. But it had never been painful. This conversation is getting more interesting by the moment!

C.J.: Almost everyone I know has a very high pain tolerance. They'll tell a story of having something happen and being very casual about it, and other people going, "No, you shouldn't be able to x, y, and z!"

Patti: How about walking around with a burst appendix for seven weeks?

C.J.: How did you survive that?

Patti: Once the appendix finished rupturing, the pain went away.

C.J.: But the infection! The appendix has bacteria in it. How did your body not go into sepsis?

Patti: I don't know. All they found in surgery was the pus because the tumor was a mucocele tumor, a mucus factory, which are very rare. And the subset of mucocele tumors that are cancerous is even rarer. I'm told there are only about 20 cases per year.

50

C.J.: Wow. So what made you decide to go for help?

Patti: Well, I had an adoption home study scheduled several hours northeast the week of Labor Day, and my hubby and I loaded up the R.V. to enjoy the weekend before my interviews in the community there. It is a beautiful little mountain town. But abdominal pain put me in the E.R. both Sunday and Monday. Despite ultrasounds and C.T. scans, they couldn't determine what it was and told me I might want to see a surgeon when I got back home. Since the pain disappeared before I left the E.R., I grabbed copies of the scans, and we relaxed for the rest of the day. Tuesday, I made appointments with my doctors back home for the next week. Part of the long wait was that the surgeon wanted me to first have a colonoscopy, then he had a business trip, and I had another out-of-town adoption home study. The surgeon never suggested I drop everything to make this a priority. By the time I went from one to the next and got onto the operating table, it was early October. As soon as the surgeon looked inside my abdomen, he closed me back up and told my husband that I likely had cancer. When I woke up, he said nobody in my city had "the skill set" needed to care for me and asked which of the three hospitals in LA I wanted to go to.

C.J.: Oh my God!

Patti: Then that surgeon put me through another round of tests, so by the time I was on their operating table, it was seven weeks of my walking around with a burst appendix, but I only had pain during the two days it was actively rupturing. So enough about my pain story, what else caught you and your team by surprise?

C.J.: The thing that surprised us was that it took our survey for anyone to make the connections and take them seriously. The survey was developed in 2016, preliminary data was received in 2017, and the final data compiled in March of 2018. The survey was published in 2020. It has been presented many times. At that time of our survey, it was 40 years since Dr. Jones made the "discovery" of FAS. That was a bit surprising, but even more so, it was disappointing. I'm encouraged, though, that our survey did create renewed interest in FASD research into a deeper understanding of FASD.

A second survey was done by the ALC on the Quality of Life in Adults with FASD, which has also been presented numerous times. The findings are still being formatted for publication with the help of a Ph.D. social work researcher. We are just about to start working on a third survey, too.

Patti: I've had that mixture of "How could this be in this day and age?" with the soul-crushing disappointment that there's not more understanding because I have this reaction with regard to type one diabetes. People being told, "You have the flu," when they go to the E.R., only to die from DKA (Diabetic Ketoacidosis). I feel that way about both conditions – T1D and FASD.

C.J.: I have a funny story. Three weeks before we were scheduled to present the preliminary findings of our survey, I dislocated my knee. I have a trick knee that goes out from time to time, and I usually reset it myself.

Patti: (grimaces)

C.J.: So I was running for the bus to get to work, and my knee came out, and the bus went sailing by. So I'm lying on the ground, and I have my phone. So I phoned work and said, "I'm going to be late for work. I've just missed my bus." When he said okay, I replied that I would probably catch the next one. And then, I attempted to pop my knee back into place. But it wouldn't go back in. Bystanders asked if I needed help, and even though I said, "No, I can fix it," someone called 911 anyway.

Patti: Well, it's just not just an ordinary thing for most people to witness.

C.J.: Exactly. So then I called home to let my mom know someone had called an ambulance, and I was on my way to the hospital. My next call was to my boss again. I said, "I don't think I'm going to be able to make my shift." And he goes, "Is the bus not coming?" I said, "No, I'm in an ambulance." I think the manager's like, well, you could have led with that... But I didn't think that was important. The important thing was I wasn't going to make it to work. In my mind, my knee wasn't important because I was used to it doing weird things. Calling off for my shift was the most important thing to say. Yeah.

Patti: (laughs) Responsible, anyway.

C.J.: Yeah. Anyway, the EMTs load me into the ambulance, and the guy asks me about my medical history. So I started by saying I've had a bilateral femur rotation.

Patti: A what?

C.J.: Both my femurs were rotated and plated into place. I like to say that the little cells got drunk when the architect was putting them on, so they were built backwards. I mean, supposedly, I'm Irish, so my builders were drunk. Things happen when you drink on the job! (laughing hard).

Patti: (laughing hard) I almost spewed my coffee! I love your sense of humor! That's actually a very good way of describing it!

C.J.: It was my first ride in an ambulance.

Patti: Just as a total aside… riding an ambulance - you'd think they'd have better shocks. I expected a much smoother ride. I'd hate for them to be starting an IV when the ambulance hit a pothole!

C.J.: So then I said I have FASD. Anyway, we get to the hospital. But because I wasn't screaming in pain, or asking for any kind of pain medication, or being hysterical, like I guess other people would be doing, I think they didn't know what to do with me. The female paramedic said (to the nurse), "Oh, she doesn't act like anybody who has FAS." I'm thinking to myself, "Oh, I'm sorry. I left my handbook (for how I should act) at home."

Patti: Yeah, no kidding!

C.J.: Oh! In the ambulance, I asked the paramedic who stayed in the back with me for some water. He said, "Do you think this Club Med?" I said, "No, I think this is an ambulance." Well, if they can't diagnose FAS from that exchange (concrete thinking), they have no business telling me how to act!

So that happened. Then the next year, we were supposed to give the full presentation.
And three weeks before that…

Patti: I sense a pattern here.

C.J.: I know. So three weeks before our second presentation, I had this weird pain. I thought it was stress or too much coffee. So the pain would double me over, and when it would stop, I'd go on with my day because what else are you going to do?

Patti: Right.

C.J.: I mean, you have things to do.

Patti: Yes, so you truck on.

C.J.: Exactly. You just keep going. And one morning, I had that weird pain again. And I said, oh, it hurts. And I went to lie down instead of going to work. My knee going out is no big deal. That doesn't hurt.

Patti: I can relate. I've broken bones without feeling significant pain and so been disbelieved. In high school, I broke my arm way up in the socket, just a hairline fracture. I was taking a shortcut to school and slipped on snow-covered steps that led to a 20-foot drop-off. So I got up as fast as I could to stop all my books from going down the cliff, then piled them on my broken arm and supported all that weight with my good arm. And nobody believed me because I wasn't a sobbing mess.

Then, in my senior year, I was rehearsing for a modern dance recital at school and landed wrong from a jump. Even though I did not experience pain, it must have at least registered on my face because the teacher pulled

54

me and made me call my mother to take me for an x-ray. I ask you, how does one break the toe *next to* the big toe and none of the others? I tell you, what's really bad is when you break your tailbone.

C.J.: I think my sister's done that.

Patti: Icy steps strike again! Broke my tailbone. You know, if you rely on public transportation, you really don't want to be carrying around a donut cushion to sit on.

C.J.: (laughs) I rely on public transportation. So when I had those stomach pains, I went to the hospital, and... Thank goodness my mom was there for me and advocating for me because I was too busy throwing up. I couldn't function because I was in so much pain. I had never felt pain like this before.

Patti: That sounds like when my appendix was exploding.

C.J.: Yeah. It turns out my intestines were tangling. They asked me to rate my pain on a scale of one to ten. I said, "Maybe a seven" because I didn't want to feel (like a drama queen). But it turns out I had cause to feel like this level of pain was traumatic. I was in surgery within six hours of arriving at the hospital.

Patti: I totally get you there, C.J. When I had my surgery six years ago, I certainly wasn't expecting to hear that they found cancer, even though the surgeon where I lived was guessing that. So let me ask you, C.J., how common is it to not feel cold weather?

C.J.: I don't know. I know that people who just don't perceive the temperature. I was the same way for a really long time. I just know. Like, (chilly vs. other people's cold). And then I got the flu really, really badly. After that, I could feel cold (the way most people do).

Patti: I'm curious because I was the kid who would never dress appropriately to go to school. It would be twenty degrees (Fahrenheit), and I'd wear a knit cape. I would walk a mile to school with a knit cape and be perfectly fine. I started thinking about this as I was learning about FASD and our sensory systems. As a foster care social worker, I can't begin to count the kids on my caseload that lost coat after coat after coat in the wintertime. Such a high preponderance of kids in foster care have prenatal exposure to alcohol. Makes you wonder, eh?

C.J.: I wonder if that's a thing. It could be.

Patti: If you don't feel cold, then walking out into cold air is not much of a reminder to turn around and get your coat.

C.J.: That's a good question that needs to be asked. I don't know how you would test that, though.

Patti: I don't either. But I think it's really interesting. I know prenatal exposure to alcohol can interfere with the brain receiving signals of hunger or fullness, so I just kind of wondered if it also could impact our ability to receive the messages that our peripheral system is sending, just as it seems to with messages of pain.

C.J.: I kind of failed science. I didn't kind of - I did fail. But because hot and cold are kind of related to pain, (so that makes sense).

Patti: That's another weird thing because, in some respects, I have a super high pain tolerance, and in other respects, I've had chronic pain conditions since 1983.

C.J.: Oh wow.

Patti: They're tied to the diabetes. One is diabetic peripheral neuropathy, which causes you to either experience burning or numbness, primarily in your feet and legs. For me, it was debilitating burning, but I always look at the glass is half-full perspective, and the silver lining in that pain cloud was that the Dept. of Vocational Rehab paid for my graduate degree. Undergraduate social workers don't earn a living wage, and I can't push myself too hard without pain shutting me down. But through the years, I got really good at ignoring the pain, just in order to function. It's funny how some pains I felt while others I did not. There were adaptive accommodations too. For instance, I learned to only enroll in morning classes because, by the middle of the day, I was toast. I had to get home and get off my feet. But that was back in the 80s. A neurologist I saw around 2005 said my nerves have kind of burnt themselves out, which is why I'm no longer living with chronic pain levels like I had been. Although there are still occasional flare-ups. Stress is a trigger, and burning the candle at both ends is a guaranteed cause of a flare-up. But the arthritis? Now that's a whole different kind of pain. Mild but unrelenting. And I definitely feel the sciatica from my degenerative disc disease. Now I'm wondering if that, too, is tied to the FASD. Mm-hmm. I'll have to look that up in your survey results.

C.J.: I know people have that. Yeah, that's no fun.

Patti: And I can't get my back repaired until after my mom passes - I can't risk having to pick her up off the floor when I'm recovering from surgery. She's a featherweight, but she's more than 10 pounds! (the post-op limit for lifting). Anyway, I listened to the podcast you did five times because there was so much information shared there. When I listened to the three of you talk about your survey, I had light bulbs going off. Ding, ding, ding, ding. I kept saying to myself, I have that, oh, I had that too!

C.J.: (laughs)

Patti: The information really answered a lot of questions for me. I'm sure you were doing your own processing of this stuff as you sat at that dinner table comparing medical stories at that conference. When all the data started rolling in, were there any a-ha moments for you?

C.J.: No, it was *validating*. It was more of a reaction like, "Okay, so it's not all in my head." My parents have been really good role models for how to advocate for what I need, whether it's a different specialist or to consider a different explanation. But I'm also very susceptible to accept a doctor's dismissal of my concerns since I have such a high pain tolerance, so it's kind of nice that the survey sparked all these studies and people are taking our higher risk of things seriously. Maybe that way, things can be treated early on without waiting till their conditions are much worse.

Patti: Is there a way that people can have access to this survey and its findings to take to their doctors without ordering the whole book?

C.J.: Our group (International ALC of the FASD Changemakers) has an e-copy of our chapter of The Rutledge Handbook of Social Work and Addictive Behaviors, where we are published, although it's a great book that is available on Amazon. (See the Appendix for ordering information).

Patti: One of the reasons why I wanted so much to talk with you, even though you've known you had FASD since childhood, rather than learning as an adult like me, is because this discussion of health might be one of the things people resonate with and begin to wonder if FASD is an explanation for their life. That they might see themselves in the discussion of having all these physical things wrong, that's the purpose of this project. So that people might see themselves through a new lens. And if it fits, then go do something about it.

C.J.: Yeah. So FASD truly is a medical diagnosis. Because so much emphasis has been placed on the learning and behavioral issues, as well as the perception of the inability to "fit in" with society – all of these things make it a very shame-based disability. But the reality is that there is a medical diagnosis behind it. FASD, like any other medical diagnosis, should be acknowledged. It should be treated. It should be accommodated. I think people are so focused on the social and learning part of it, which is a big part of it. But they treat it more as a social thing, like a social issue instead of a medical issue. That is so disappointing.

Patti: But I'm wondering if perhaps the hesitancy to recognize the medical aspects of FASD is because, you know, no one really started looking at that until your survey findings came out.

C.J.: I can understand it, though. On the one hand, if there are behavioral issues, learning challenges, early childhood trauma, and drinking in the home… why would you look at the medical side? You're too busy building safety nets, hopefully. But on the other hand, the other issue is blame.

People tend to think once someone has become an adult, all those struggles magically go away. You're supposed to understand everything and to be able to function in society. Where are all the adults with FASD (in the minds of the general public)? Only these pitiful children. No one stops to think that those same children have grown up.

Patti: I can relate to that in a couple of different ways. I think of all the kids that I've worked with through almost a quarter century working in child welfare. I've watched two decades' worth of kids fall through the cracks. Because they were misdiagnosed or partially diagnosed, they were diagnosed with ADHD or reactive attachment disorder, or this or that. But there's no consideration at all to the fact that so many are in the system due to prenatal exposure to toxins, whether alcohol or drugs, which affects the brain and how it functions. Well, infant screenings are done for primarily for illegal drugs. But alcohol is not screened with that test. Alcohol screenings are far more expensive, and the rationalization is that a baby is "pos-tox" for all these other things. That's a good enough reason to detain the baby and give the mom a case plan. Consider also that alcohol also happens to be legal. So why waste resources testing for something that is legal? And why would birth parents, who are already being judged, admit to more than they have to, let alone admit to something that's legal to use?

My practice as a social worker was revolutionized – it hit me that most of the kids I've worked with had invisible physical disabilities that were unrecognized, and therefore, unaccommodated. It may not come as a surprise to you that over time, social workers become very cynical, and when children are reunited with their parents, a great many times it is with a sigh and the comment, "Give it time, we'll see them again." Here's why: exposure to drugs, alcohol, and trauma literally injures a child's brain. It will affect them for life to varying degrees.

Are the parents taught how to work with their child's brain injury? How it affects their son or their daughter? Of course not! Not when no one in the system sees past the outward behavior to its underlying cause! So the children lose out on equitable support. The parents lose out because they are not prepared to get their children back and to do well with them. Even the foster parents lose out because no one adequately prepares them either. They get frustrated and demand the child be moved to another home, which re-traumatizes the child, and shreds what little ability to attach they had built up. It is no wonder why these kids fall through the cracks! Because you can't outgrow physical disabilities. I never outgrew my "juvenile" diabetes. I stopped being a juvenile decades ago, but I'm still diabetic. You can't outgrow FASD, either.

C.J.: I suspect also that the medical issues that people were seeing in adults with FASD have been attributed a lot to other things. There's a lot of judgment around the catch-all phrase "lifestyle." I don't think being addicted to drugs and alcohol and having horrific childhoods is a lifestyle. The word "lifestyle" implies that you chose it.

Patti: I worked in drugs and alcohol for the first several years of my career in the early 1990s. And I never met a single person to ever wake up in the morning and say, "I think I'm going to become an addict today."

C.J.: Exactly. No woman says to herself, "I'm going to consciously harm my baby by drinking today. I'm going to choose to damage my child's brain and body, and I don't care." No one does that! We are hardwired to protect our children.

Patti: Exactly. But the stigma persists because, you know, as a society, we judge mothers for drinking. And yet, we disregard all the advertising that makes drinking look cool and hip – there's no getting away from it. If we don't watch T.V., the ads are on billboards. When we are tempted to judge a mom for drinking during pregnancy, we're not stopping to remind ourselves that one-third of women keep getting periods throughout the first trimester. So why would they suspect they are pregnant? Why would they stop their social drinking?

C.J.: Right.

Patti: We're not thinking about how far the average woman is when she suspects and gets confirmation that she's pregnant. What kind of damage is already done to that baby? Significant damage. We mentioned before that babies develop the changes to their facial features when mom consumes alcohol between days 17-21. That's well before most women know that they are pregnant.

60

C.J.: Yeah. There was a 2014 article in Cosmo, "I drank while pregnant." The author knew all the facts, but she didn't think a few drinks (would hurt her child). She'd ignore the judgmental looks she would get and tell herself it would be fine. The article ended with the baby being healthy at birth. That it didn't do any harm.

Patti: So the baby had all her fingers and toes, a strong heartbeat, and breathed well. There's more to being healthy than that! There's no way to tell at birth how the wiring in that baby's brain was altered. Where's the follow-up article? Is that child now able to process abstract thoughts? Process information or language quickly? Regulate his or her emotions? Make decisions or predictions? I could go on, ad nauseum.

C.J.: And I'm thinking she's among a set of women who think FASD could never happen to them because of the myths they believe. Unfortunately, many believe that you have to be alcoholic. They believe that you have to be a "certain kind" of woman. This woman was white, upper class, and drank wine. And she was not ashamed, and she went to Cosmo. The article was written in 2014. So it's a while ago. But it serves to remind us that there are women out there who truly do not believe that they're doing harm to their baby. Or to their children. And I know my mother didn't. She had no clue.

Patti: The scare tactics don't work if you think they don't apply to you. Part of what's wrong in our society is all the "othering" that we do. Some people call it tribalism. By holding on to those myths that only certain types of people have to worry about FASD, you can other away everything. It doesn't apply to me because blah blah blah. One of the things I learned at FASCETS is that the most at-risk woman bringing FASD about in their children are middle to upper-class, college-educated white women because they're othering – FASD affects other women. I don't see myself in various populations. Therefore, it's not my concern. And if their obstetrician says a glass of wine here and there is safe, then the myth is reinforced.

C.J.: Yes, their children are diagnosed with ADHD or Autism. But what if those are only partial diagnoses?

Patti: Yes, the reality is that you can have FASD *and* the other diagnoses children receive. If you look up the diagnostic criteria for Autism, you will find that 100% of those behavioral characteristics *also* fall under FASD. Same with ADHD. I'm not qualified to say it is one vs. the other, but please, people, recognize that it can be both.

C.J.: Yep. And. If the child is diagnosed with something other than FASD, then they don't have to carry the FASD stigma around with them, or their parents don't have to face the stigma and the judgment.

Patti: But, you know, and I am so thankful that there is such a large lobby for those on the autism spectrum. I'm so thankful for that because they need it. They need support and resources. They need to be understood. But that doesn't change the fact that anyone could have both things going on. Just because you have one does not rule out the other.

C.J.: And that's something that doesn't have a "cause." I think a lot of medical professionals take the position of providing a partial diagnosis: if adequate services through the other diagnoses are available, run with that one. That way, services are in place without causing stigma.

Patti: Yes, but that's ultimately not fair to the child. If *only* the autism spectrum or the ADHD, the Obsessive Compulsive, and the Oppositional Defiant disorders are diagnosed, then a child who was prenatally exposed won't understand what's happening physically if they develop any of the comorbid conditions that came out from your survey!

C.J.: And it's not fair to the woman who admits to drinking and whose child has FASD. Services are tied to diagnoses. If services are provided around a partial diagnosis, will they be adequate? If they are not adequate for the child, then the parent also suffers. No one is in a vacuum. Stigma is a barrier to properly diagnosing children. How are we supposed to appropriately treat someone without a thorough diagnosis? Nobody would say, "Oh, you know, breast cancer is so shameful. Let's just call yours ovarian cancer. They're both cancer, but you won't have to feel shame." There's so many reasons why things like that matter, where actual diagnoses matter—and getting the right treatment matters. But nobody seems to care about FASD in this way.

It's unethical. It is unethical and immoral. People want to talk about morality of causes and drinking. It is immoral for society to not acknowledge the big elephant in the room, which is alcohol. Yeah. We're okay drinking it. We're okay partying. We're okay advertising it.

Patti: But other than DUI billboards, no one points out the consequences.

C.J.: The alcohol industry is allowed to peddle their product because they have a warning label on them, but they also put the onus on somebody else all the time. Really, just how effective is the labeling, anyway?

Patti: I think of the warning on a pack of cigarettes. The label warns pregnant women that the product can cause low birth weight. Well, so what? Let's get real. Would it not be more effective to warn pregnant women that tobacco is the number one cause of ADHD, according to Dr. Ira Chasnoff? Of course, that would be more effective because women want their children to be free of the challenges of ADHD.

C.J.: People did go after the cigarette industry and have shifted the culture away from cigarettes, though people still smoke. I don't know if you can go after the liquor industry and be as successful. I think they need to, but I don't think it's going to happen. I think there have been attempts. And it's just been shot down. Governments legalize addictive substances and behaviors for the tax dollars. It would be nice if we (FASD Advocates) could leverage some of that taxation.

Patti: Yes, like with cigarettes. A chunk of the taxes supposedly goes to address the high medical costs associated with lung cancer, often caused by cigarettes, which is, if it happens, really cool. Lottery taxes supposedly help cover the costs of public education. If the taxes from alcohol sales could go toward FASD diagnostic and support services, that would be *huge!* Currently, supports for those with FASD tends to evaporate when the child ages out to adulthood. But you don't outgrow developmental disabilities. Some of us function well on our own, while others will need lifelong supports in place. Those of us living with FASD did not choose this; we are not to blame, so it is not fair to not provide us with resources and supports.

But we have to deal with it anyway, just like any other medical diagnosis we are faced with.

C.J.: I get nervous when conversations happen around who pays for what because, ultimately, it turns back to the blame game, and everyone blames the moms. We're back to the stigma. Unfortunately, FASD is going to happen. Just like people who smoke are going to smoke. FASD is going to happen as long as there is alcohol. I'd like to see the rates of FASD go down. That would be lovely. But I'd *really* like the stigma to go away because nobody hurts their baby on purpose. Women who drink during pregnancy either don't know they're pregnant yet or believe the myth that one or two drinks are safe or the myth that it is safe to "drink till it's pink." You know, when you speed down a highway, you're not thinking, "I'm going to crash." You're thinking, "This is fun." But there are consequences.

Patti: Yes. Today's generation tends to be short-sighted and live in the moment. They don't think of the consequences. One of the issues that many of us with FASD face is the inability to recognize consequences and tie them to our actions. So let's look at this. So we know alcohol use tends to run in families. We tend to do what is modeled to us. So, if I had a child with FASD, whether or not it was recognized and supports were offered, then is anyone looking at me as more than a perpetrator? Is anyone recognizing that there is a very high likelihood that I also have FASD from my mother and so on? So my lack of judgment may have been biologically based. And hers before me. Not to mention that anything that impacts a baby's development in the womb also affects the development of the woman's grandchildren if the baby is female because the developing female's eggs for that next generation are formed before that baby is even born! So any sip of alcohol affects not only that little girl who's being formed but also any of her children. People don't consider that when they are making decisions about what they put in their bodies.

C.J.: And that's not even counting the impact from what men are doing prior to conception. Sperm are stored for three months. So what dad does impacts babies through epigenetics or the coding on the outside of the DNA.

Patti: Yes, and it absolutely contributes to a baby's development. But there again, people are just living in the moment. People don't understand how alcohol is more harmful than cocaine to a baby! Alcohol is a teratogen; it not only crosses the placental barrier to affect the baby, but it passes through the baby's blood-brain barrier and affect the way the brain cells develop. The alcohol molecule is much smaller than the molecules of several of these other drugs and so does a lot more damage because it gets in a lot more places. It is said that prenatal exposure to alcohol creates "swiss cheese brain." Personally, I think the alcohol warning labels need to say: If you are capable of becoming pregnant, you shouldn't drink. Just like when you go to a medical center before you get an X-ray, you have to answer a question about being pregnant. Could you be pregnant? When was your last period? If you're in an emergency room and they need to do radiographs, they don't trust your answer; they do a pregnancy test before they do the scan for that very reason. So I think, from a prevention standpoint, we need to make it very clear that if you're of childbearing years, then be very purposeful in your family planning.

C.J.: In 2014, the CDC came out with the advice that if you're female, maybe you shouldn't drink because you could be pregnant. And the Late Show took that and ran with it, mocking the advice and making women "drinking like a man" into almost a badge of honor. It seems to be some sort of weird female emancipation thing. And it's treated as a symbol of freedom (from feminine oppression). Yeah. I have the equal right to get totally smashed, but why would I want that?

Patti: What does that prove? There's so many cultural aspects to drinking. It's an important message, C.J. It's totally important to bring it out there, not to blame parents for their child's struggles, but to blame the substance, especially because alcohol is legal. People assume that because alcohol and marijuana are legal, they are safe. But they're not. And certainly not prudent if you're going to drive or conceive children. But again, state governments legalize addictive substances and behaviors so they can profit off of people's addictions via the taxes they collect. So what are some of the other myths, C.J., that really get you kind of going?

C.J.: There are so many myths. Thinking that FASD only affects children is one - that you just somehow grow out of it.

Patti: Um, I think the snappy comeback to that myth would be, "Oh, can you outgrow Downs Syndrome as well?"

C.J.: Exactly. Except with Downs Syndrome, you have "the face," and that's another myth of FASD – that you have to have the facial features. I have every single one. But for some reason, because my face doesn't look like a young child's face, people don't recognize the features.

Patti: I have the eyes. Very small eye openings. I never knew I had any of the facial characteristics. But looking back, I wonder if I "should" have figured it out earlier in life. Every time I go to the eye doctor, they constantly tell me to open (my eyes) wider.

Are there any other myths that drive you nuts?

C J: Another myth is it only happens to other people.

Patti: Yeah. We talked a fair bit about that one already.

C.J.: and that FASD is not common.

Patti: That one drives me nuts too! The pre-Covid statistics are that FASD impacts 5% of the general population and, according to Barb Clark, parent support coordinator for the North American Council on Adoptable Children (NACAC), 80% of children within the foster care system. People with FASD are everywhere! We're talking, a minimum of one child in every classroom, a minimum of one of your neighbors on your block. Statistically speaking, anyway. But in response to the pandemic lockdowns, alcohol sales saw an increase of 20%, and alcohol consumption by women jumped up 41%. Guaranteed, the prevalence is more than one in twenty people now.

C.J.: Oh, yeah. We're everywhere in every stratum of society. You know, if alcohol is used by every ethnicity and race, culture, and economic stratum, which it is, then FASD is present in every sub-population also. Here's another myth-buster: you do not have to be an alcoholic to have a child with a FASD. Social drinkers give birth to babies with FASD all the time. Alcohol will damage the brain and body of a child, no matter how small the dose. Wherever alcohol is consumed, the consequences, including FASD, follow. I would also say that people conflate FASD with the effects of trauma. FASD in itself is not trauma.

Patti: I would agree with that, but people don't understand our behavior reflects the way we are prewired to respond, which is different for everybody. We end up getting blamed, shamed, and punished for behavior that's biologically based. That is in itself traumatic.

C.J.: Yeah, and I think that's because the effects of alcohol exposure are so varied among individuals. I mean, we're all different.

Patti: We're all uniquely wired to be able to complete various cognitive functions, or brain tasks, that underlie any given behavior. Each person's particular combination of challenges and strengths is as unique as their fingerprint.

C.J.: Yeah.

Patti: If we can drive home that message, I think that will go a fair amount toward busting up some of those myths.

C.J.: I agree. Another myth is that we're going to live a hopeless life. Growing up, the myths were that you wouldn't get far in life, you won't hold a job, you're going to end up in jail, you're going to end up on the street, you're going to end up X, Y, and Z. And that did happen to a majority of people when I was young. And no one really questioned why it was or the surrounding factors, only that the commonality between all these people was that they had an FASD. I am grateful and thankful, and lucky. I am lucky, above all, to have not experienced that. Yeah. I have been very lucky (to have the adoptive parents that I did). My mom and my dad put a safety net around me. As a teen, I hated having FASD. On the inside, I just wanted to crawl out of my skin and die. I mean, obviously, not literally.

Patti: Right.

C.J.: But if I could have just shed that part of me, I would have. People think that as soon as you're in your twenties, things are going to be great. You're going to have all this freedom. No. You're going to develop the skills for that level of enjoyment in your 30s. And I have to say, my thirties have been awesome.

Patti: The forties were my favorite decade. My forties were fabulous. My fifties? Not so nifty. (Chuckles)

C.J.: Well, my thirties have been pretty fantastic, I'd have to say. I'm comfortable with myself. Yeah. I do have challenges. I can't drive. (When you face your limitations), I mean, you have to cry, scream, rail against the world, and cry out how not fair it is. But sooner or later, you're going to have to look (at things the way they are). The best chance you have in life is (through) acceptance. Acceptance that you're not going to be like everybody else. The measures of success that you or somebody else places on you are not going to be your measures of success. The most successful thing you can be is you. And if you're on financial assistance, you're on financial assistance. So what? You can still live a quality life. If you get up in the morning, you make your bed. And you remember your pills. Count that success. If you're addicted to something, and you get up in the morning, and you decide not to (use something), if you hold off the urge, hold off that call of drinking or doing drugs for even ten minutes, that's a success.

Patti: That's why in recovery, they emphasize the importance of living one day at a time. And sometimes it's one hour at a time. Sometimes it's one moment at a time. Addictions are all about the brain too. Despite having worked in the field (of addictions) for several years, I've never really been comfortable with the disease model. Because so much of it is brain-based, it has to do with dopamine receptivity. There are other things that can activate that.

C.J.: It's not. We don't have to moralize it. And we also don't have to medical model it. Drinking is not a moral issue. Not providing services for your community is a moral and ethical issue. You're only as strong as your weakest member. And if you're forgoing one in every twenty people, if you're telling them they're not worth it because FASD is "largely preventable."

Patti: We can talk about the message of preventability for a while. For now, I would say that yes, once women are aware that they are pregnant, they do have choice as to what they put into their bodies; but the only effective prevention is to totally abstain from alcohol during childbearing years, and let's face it, *that* is not realistic.

C.J.: (Exactly, but for us, as the children,) we didn't cause it within ourselves. So to write off giving us supports is grossly unfair. I think it is (rationalized) by a biblical belief that the sins of X are visited upon the children. And if it's caused, then you deserve this because you did this. I think a lot of society, whether they want to admit it or not, is based on a very narrow view of a structure that was in power for a very long time.

Patti: So, as a woman of faith, I would say the proper way to interpret that verse is not the condemnation of the sin being visited upon the next umpteen generations as an ongoing moral issue, but rather the effects of that sin. We see this in the study of Adverse Childhood Experiences. The repercussions of our actions influence family dynamics, and that becomes a vehicle for intergenerational trauma, whether we are talking about alcohol addiction or anything else. Even a poor diet can affect the entire family and go down through the generations. The effects are intergenerational. Any justification of withholding services from this "biblical standard" is spiritual abuse. I'm accountable for the things that I have chosen to do in life, the things I've chosen to say in life, and the things I have omitted to do or say when I knew better. But I am not accountable for the actions of my brother or my uncle, let alone my ancestors. However, I still have to deal with the effects of other people's choices: these effects are not moral issues. I deal with the repercussions of my mother's nightly glass of wine, just as I deal with everything else in life because it's part of living. But as a society, don't we owe it to each other to make sure that we are as healthy as we can be, simply because our actions *do impact* others?

C.J.: I'm not a person of faith, but I have obviously respect for people who are because they know something I don't. I understand things differently. I never want my ignorance to be interpreted as offense. We all have our own understanding of things.

Patti: Whether we're talking about faith, or anything else, we can and must respect each person's right to their own opinion. All of us view the world through our own unique lens of our experiences. I think there's that whole issue about rights, personal or individual rights versus societal rights. You know the medical ethic of "do no harm?" It applies to living in general as well. Do no harm. We have the right to make choices in life, but we do not have the right to harm others by our actions. We must become sensitive to the impacts of our choices. If a woman drinks before she knows she is pregnant, we cannot hold her accountable for what she was unaware of, while we *can* blame the alcohol itself. Meanwhile, if we each can help prevent harm by what we are doing with our projects that each of us have going on, then we're doing a good thing.

C.J.: Yeah. I think another myth regarding having facial features, is you won't be okay. That's a myth. You *will* be okay. We're not defective. Our brains and our bodies were changed by the alcohol, but that doesn't mean that we're defective. Yes, it's a physical disability. It's a medical disability. It has behavioral symptoms. It has ramifications with learning and intellect for some of us. But it doesn't mean that we're defective. It doesn't mean that there's something wrong. It doesn't mean that we're less than. It just means that we're different.

Patti: And that's the beauty of the movement towards neurodiversity. Everybody sees things differently. We're all wired uniquely and have differing combinations of interests and strengths as well as challenges. Wouldn't the world be boring if we were all the same? Different roles are best filled by those gifted in different areas. Society needs *every* role. Many professions would not be where they are without the creativity of neurodivergent people like us being in them. We tend to think outside the box, so to speak. Because otherwise, there would be no growth and development, and life would have been stagnant. Could we have had the industrial revolution without people with those strengths, gifts, and talents? No.

C.J.: Yeah. Look at what happens when only one kind of person is valued. Yeah. We have learned.

Patti: Exactly, any of the genocides history has witnessed, from the atrocities committed against indigenous populations to the Holocaust. We must all agree: Never Again! But on a smaller scale, those who are neurodivergent, like those of us with FASD, have often been the targets of bullying. The reasons for our "differentness" is generally not visible, and many of us function well in life, though that does not mean we are without challenges caused by alcohol exposure.

C.J.: And that's another myth: the myth of high functioning vs. low functioning. Because of people's perception of "high functioning" leads to assumptions that you can be "independent." If you function well on day A, you should be able to be functional on Day B because you're "high functioning." There is no high or low functioning. There is just everyone doing the best they can in life.

Patti: That's so very true. I think the stigma continues because people fear judgment from others. People say, "Oh, you can't have FASD" because I have advanced degrees and a good career. Nonetheless, there are areas in life that I am definitely impacted. I benefit from external structure, and that is the basis of the approach I use in working with folks. Together, we figure out where tailored supports are needed and put them into place. This ties back to the myth you brought up earlier about needing to have "the face" (characteristic facial features of FAS) – that you have to look or act a certain way to have FASD. And similarly, we talked earlier about the myth that only indigenous peoples are impacted by FASD. So if we're not in that population, we don't have to worry.

C.J.: Not seeing it in ourselves because we obviously don't fit that other category, whatever that category happens to be, yes. You can see that neither of us are indigenous. I'm part Irish with reddish hair. In 2012, I had a social worker come into the house. She should have known better. She starts pointing at my children and asking, "Which one of you are real, and which one of you are being fostered?"

Patti: (Looks aghast and sharply draws in a breath.)

C.J.: It gets worse. We're talking about disability. I say I have FAS. And then she goes, "Oh, are you aboriginal?" I've had other issues with that particular social worker, and I had made a formal complaint.

Patti: Good.

C.J.: My complaint was for something else that I had witnessed. She turned around and blamed me, claiming the situation had been my fault because I have FAS. Thankfully, she went for retraining for like the biggest time. But the fact that she absolutely believed that you had to be indigenous! Sadly, tragically, a lot of people believe that.

Patti: One of my favorite phrases is: nobody knew what they didn't know until they learned it. And everybody learns things in a different order and at a different pace. C.J., it has been so wonderful talking with you today. Thank you for so generously sharing your story and your thoughts about what people need to know about FASD.

Putting the Pieces Together as a Teen
A Conversation with Emily Hargrove

In this conversation, I speak with Mrs. Emily Hargrove, PhD candidate, APPA accredited philosophical counselor, published researcher, speaker, wife, mother, Pastor, and Jesus Lover. Emily is a member of the International Adult Leadership Collaborative (ALC) of the FASD Changemakers. As the owner of Emily Hargrove Consulting – Where Faith and FASD Collide, Emily offers speaking services, philosophical counseling, and an FASD-inspired clothing and accessory line.

Patti: Emily, thank you so much for partnering with me in this project. I really appreciate your time. I know you've known of your diagnosis since you were young, so you have words of wisdom for those of us just coming into this knowledge that will be helpful. Perhaps, let's start with your story?

Emily: So I was diagnosed at a Neurodevelopmental Research Clinic at Vanderbilt when I was one year old. I had all the classic signs; everything was there and needed for a diagnosis. I had been adopted out of East St. Louis after spending a week in the hospital detoxing from all the drugs and alcohol in my system at birth. My adoptive parents noticed in that first year of development that there were some things that weren't quite right. For one, when I was a year old, I only weighed 11 pounds, and I was not gaining weight. 11 pounds at one year of age is a *little* baby.

Patti: Tiny!

Emily: So that was one of the telltale signs. They knew that I was born addicted to alcohol and other things, and they knew that my life-giving mother drank pretty much every day. But even though they had all of these pieces, back in 1992, FASD wasn't being talked about. So my parents took me from doctor to doctor, from clinician to clinician, and nothing was sticking as far as a diagnosis. The doctors thought my parents were not feeding me enough. My parents insisted that they were and that something was not right. My sleeping was odd too. Babies tend to wake up throughout the night, and that's something that parents struggle with, but not mine. My parents had to forcefully wake me each morning for a feeding. When I was one year old, I was diagnosed with growth hormone deficiency and full FAS. That was the "a-ha" (the vindication)! But my parents weren't told anything about my needs, just the name of the diagnosis and the grim prognosis. "You know, she's probably going to struggle in school. She might have this and that. She's probably not going to make it too far," etc., etc. And so that was it. They didn't offer any interventions. So my parents relied on the grace of God, and all of the things they were already doing without realizing were beneficial things.

Patti: And that is the grace of God, isn't it?

Emily: Yes! They kept me in enriching environments and activities. I started learning piano at the age of four. I started learning Spanish at the age of six. I was in martial arts, gymnastics, and all of these different environments that help build plasticity of the brain. I had not necessarily known that I was different throughout all of these years. I had known I was adopted, but not about the FAS. My parents were always very open about my adoption, but they didn't set me down and say, "Hey, you have fetal alcohol syndrome." When I was approximately fifteen or sixteen, somewhere in there, that's when I learned that I had the diagnosis. I started researching it on my own. It was *my* "a-ha" moment. It was that "This is it! This explains everything!" When I talk about it to groups, I always explain that if felt like I had been floating along this path in life and lacked any weights to pull me down and make me feel grounded. So whenever I would learn little bits and pieces of who I was, whether that was my biological or life-giving family story or the fact that I have fetal alcohol syndrome... those became weights that held me down and made me feel more grounded in who I was and helped to explain why different things happened in my life and why I felt a little bit different but didn't have the words or the knowledge to provide context, so to speak. Yeah. And that is quite the journey, is it not?

Patti: It certainly is! I didn't figure out I was on the spectrum until I was fifty-four, almost fifty-five. Prior to that, I had come up with other explanations for things in life. Such as, why kids rejected me, bullied me, and why I never felt like I fit in, that kind of thing. Once I learned that I had an FASD that explained everything a whole lot better. Throughout my youth, I had blamed it all on my diabetes, setting me apart, but understanding what I do now about FASD, it is a far better explanation! Knowing the diagnosis doesn't change me in any way, but having the right explanation really does make a difference on an emotional level.

Emily: Absolutely. I know that the ALC always (draw the analogy to other) medical diagnoses in the sense that maybe you break a bone in your body. For example, if you go throughout your whole life being told that you had sprained your ankle, and so you got treated for a sprain, but the whole time, it was really a broken bone. Once you realize, oh no, it was actually broken, then you get the right treatment or the right intervention.

Patti: In the case of FASD, the right understanding brings clarity to your life story.

Emily: But when you get that correct diagnosis, and it is a *medical* diagnosis, then it's where things start to make sense and where we can apply appropriate interventions.

Patti: My hope is that people will get their first clue about their own effects of prenatal exposure to alcohol by reading this book. Many readers are about to embark on this journey too.

Emily: I present to a lot of different audiences. Sometimes the audiences know that they have a diagnosis, and others may merely suspect that they do. Or it might be completely fresh, too - completely a new thought. But every time I'm explaining some of my journey, some of my story, and some of my struggles, some of my brain struggles, some of my physical struggles — to watch the light bulb go off is incredible. But then I always, always,

always couple that with self-compassion, understanding, and with this idea that any perceived quality of life should never preside over the sanctity of life. Sanctity meaning value. And so I always bring back to this idea that regardless of the quality of life, someone else may speak over us, or we may feel that we have our value doesn't change. And that also goes for our life-giving mothers as well. And so there's also this other side of it that people have to journey through this. It's so often described as grief for a lot of people. I never had this sense of grief or anger toward my life-giving mother.

Patti: "Life-giving mother." In all my years of being an adoption home study writer and adoption social worker, I've never heard that before. I absolutely love that!

Emily: Me too! Someone shared that with me, and I was blown away because it restores dignity back to the person that gave us life. I mean, she is the reason why we are here, part of the reason, at least. So acknowledging that sanctity of life still presides over the quality of life, I think, is still in that journey. Then there's this other piece of it, that if you go on the internet, or if you go to a conference, because now you're curious (about FASD), then you're immediately hit in the face with negative prognoses. And you're immediately hit in the face with all the things you're (supposedly) not going to be able to accomplish. So part of what I do is acknowledge that, yes, there's going to be struggle, but every single person struggles. But there is hope, there is help, and there is healing. All of these things can be for everyone. So that's also a part of the journey, is to be self-compassionate, to be patient in that journey, and to acknowledge that it is okay to sit in grief or anger for a moment, always remembering that there is hope on the other side of that.

As a side story, when I first started dating my husband, I told him that I'm passionate about educating and self-advocating for fetal alcohol spectrum disorders, then explained what it is. After that conversation, he turned to Google, which highlighted a study that was conducted in Canada. According to that study, the average age of the individual to pass away in a hospital with FASD, in this study, was thirty-four. But that was based on *one* study, with proper context being set. Many do not have health problems

76

while they are young, however. Fetal alcohol spectrum disorders are real, and the struggle is too. I have plenty of friends (with FASD) that live past the age of thirty-four.

Patti: (pointing at self)

Emily: CJ, she says a beautiful thing, that fetal alcohol spectrum disorder is not the end. It's not. And *I say* it's the beginning of understanding.

Patti: Thirty-four. So, I'm almost thirty years past that. I'll be sixty this coming fall (2023). But I've had that faulty prognosis before. I was diagnosed on my second birthday with type 1 diabetes, and my pediatrician painted such a grim prognosis of my life with diabetes that my parents actually argued: my father, may he rest in peace, actually advocated for my mom to starve me to death because he didn't want to see me suffer all the things that the doctors were telling them were in my future. Naturally, I'm very glad that she won that argument. But according to the doctors, I was not supposed to live past eight years old. But here I am. I am decades past my "expiration date." And wow, here I am doing it again, way past thirty-four. So I think that we should remember that the search engine's life expectancy prediction is the product of only one study but also that, similarly to any medical diagnosis, our understanding of FASD keeps evolving. We keep learning about things. I've long said that back in the '60s, when I came along and when my parents were painted this grim picture, we really were in the medical dark ages. And, you know, FAS wasn't "discovered" until 1973. Of course, it's been around as long as alcohol has been around, so thousands of years, but nobody knew it was a thing until Dr. Jones figured it out in 1973. So search engines and everyone else are going to take a while to catch up.

Emily: I think another huge piece that comes up a lot is that whenever you use a search engine, you're hit with the message that FASD is 100% preventable.

Patti: No, it's not.

Emily: That's such a damaging message. Because if you're a person on the spectrum and you read that, (it's interpreted as) "Oh, I was preventable," or "Oh, I'm broken, and I need fixing." I think that's another part of this message to people that are just discovering their diagnosis is, "No, you are not broken. You do not need fixing. You need understanding." And alcohol is always going to be around. It's always going to exist, and we never know the full circumstance behind someone's pregnancy or behind someone's conception. We can't fully know that. So this idea that it's 100% preventable is damaging. And I'm guilty. I'm guilty of saying that in the past because that was the message of the past. But now we've moved towards a message of equity.

Patti: Which is not to say that we should not emphasize prevention. We should with any cause of brain injury because that's what FASD is. It's brain injury. Any brain injury prevention will be a worthy effort, but it will never be 100% because there's absolutely no way to do that.

Emily: And I've always objected to that phrase (100% preventable) for the sake of life-giving mothers. They don't need to beat themselves up. They should not be stigmatized the way many of them are made to feel.

Patti: That absolutely should not happen. I really appreciate, though, the point that you're bringing out in this conversation about the message that FASD is 100% preventable sends to *us*, the people living with FASD.

Emily: You know, it's in our weaknesses. That's where His (God's) grace abides. I think it's very important that we don't find our identity in our diagnosis. (Our diagnosis) might explain a lot of things, but it is not who you are. It's a part of your story. It's not your *essence*. At the same time, we can't use our diagnosis as a crutch for everything.

Patti: Very true! So often people use their diagnosis as a scapegoat to justify their actions and then blame the consequences on their diagnosis.

Emily: We need to be careful of that as well. That's not to say that we shouldn't advocate for ourselves, and we shouldn't try to find accommodations because we deserve those. We deserve accommodations, just like a blind person deserves a seeing-eye dog or any other diagnosis deserves their accommodation. FASD deserves accommodations as well. So I'm not saying you shouldn't fight for your rights and for your accommodations and for inclusion, but we should also be careful not to put our entire identity in that. I believe that our identity should come in and through the one that created us. And so if we can look outside of FASD and discover who we are outside of FASD, (to see that we are) beyond that, more than that. That (perspective) helps the journey as well. When we can start to lean on the One who created us, when we do that, our purpose is fully understood. And we can start to fully chase after that purpose. So part of the journey in discovering who we are and discovering that we have a diagnosis is perhaps in discovering our full purpose as well.

Patti: Absolutely! And I'm thinking it's fairly common for those of us who learn later in life that FASD is part of our story. So many of the folks I've talked to are furthering the cause for the FASD community by educating, advocating, or what have you. For me, it has become the focus of my work. As a professional development trainer, I help those who will play a supporting role shift from a behavioral/compliance paradigm to one that normalizes neurodiversity and understands behavior from a brain-based perspective, making some of the expectations placed upon their clients unrealistic and downright harmful. As a coach, I help neurodivergent adults methodically explore the impacts of what their brain injury has caused and how to tailor accommodations to make life go smoother. Similarly, I do the same for parents and caregivers of those affected. I have long believed, just from having grown up with a chronic condition that can turn acute on a dime, that the very moment I have finished doing the work that my Creator has put me here to do, He'll let me rest in Him. So, let me ask you, Emily, what are you doing?

Emily: So, I'm a PhD candidate, and my dissertation is on fetal alcohol spectrum disorders and spiritual development.

Patti: Oh, wonderful.

Emily: Yes, trying to better understand the spiritual lives and faith development of individuals with an FASD. So often, I think that (the spiritual) part of development is overlooked. Spiritual development is valuable as well, not just developmental or behavioral. I am also a member of the ALC or the International Adult Leadership Committee of the FASD Changemakers. We strengthen autobiographical voices in research. We search to build connections globally so that individuals, adults specifically with an FASD, can feel included and welcomed at the table. I work in the advocacy education arena of fetal alcohol spectrum disorders. Research communities must get better at inclusion and at hearing our voice. In the research world, in the advocacy world, and in communities that *say* they're for individuals with FASD and *say* that we're welcome at the table – they often are not. They ask for our stories, and they like to use our stories (anecdotally), but then they say, "Okay, now it's time for the grown-ups to talk," and they dismiss us. They use our ideas for themselves (without really listening long enough to value our input). But I don't want to turn this conversation into the negative. Members of the ALC are united in saying that we deserve a *full* seat at the table where our ideas and our essence is fully valued. At the ALC, we frequently say, *"Nothing about us, without us!"* We're saying, hey, we're here, and we are valuable, and we have ideas.

Patti: You just launched something, didn't you?

Emily: I did! I launched Emily Hargrove Consulting. My tagline is "where faith and FASD collide."

Patti: Oh, I love that!

Emily: So I offer philosophical counselling that is very FASD-aware, of course. I offer speaking services as well and an FASD-inspired clothing and accessory line. Of course, I'm excited about it.

Patti: I can't wait to see what you've got.

Emily: I said (to myself), you know what? I'd like stylish clothing that also advocates for FASD.

Patti: Yeah, I have a drawer full of Tee shirts and sweatshirts that do that for type 1 diabetes. So I think it's time that I have some for FASD too.

Emily: I don't typically bring this part up of my story because I feel like it was a lifetime ago, but what really got me started in FASD advocacy world was the Miss America Organization. When I was Miss Illinois Outstanding Teen, Miss Illinois Teen, back in the day, I got involved for the scholarship money, but I stayed for the community involvement and service aspect. The Illinois affiliate of NOFAS somehow (again, I believe it was a God thing) discovered that I had fetal alcohol syndrome. So they invited me to come and speak at their annual conference that year, and I shared my story with their audience. Ever since then, whatever pageant I competed in or represented, I used fetal alcohol syndrome as my platform. I brought awareness of FASD through just that particular avenue. I always try to encourage people to find their platform – we all have a platform. And our platform might change over time. My husband and I are next-generation pastors (grade six through college students), and so right now, my platform is to speak into the lives of the next generation, to light the fire in them to walk out their purpose with intention. And so I guess where I was going with that is that, you know, we all have different seasons in life, so our platforms (change too). But I always bring in the FAS because I think it's important. I believe that's a calling in my life. I think, in many ways, we are called to the challenges that we have because our purpose and our circumstances are so intricately webbed.

Patti: Absolutely! I never did any advocacy at all until I ended up needing to get a service dog. When my service dog and I started going out in public together, I began to experience the pushback that people get when their disability is invisible. That's also when I discovered the power of community and of cultivating friendships with similarly challenged people - just to keep one another encouraged and to be "God with skin on" for those emotional moments that we all have upon occasion. There's a lot of power in the Type I community, and I think there is with FASD as well. Emily, what are your favorite places where you find community with others who are on this journey?

Emily: I don't get to find other adults in my area that have an FASD. In part, I live in a community that still refuses to recognize it. So there's shame and stigma still surrounding it. So one message to adults just discovering (their FASD) is that they might run into the shame and stigma. It depends on where you are. It depends on which community you're a part of. There are so many different moving pieces to this (question). So I have this... for a church community, for example... I love being involved in the church community, obviously. I don't think I would be a pastor if I didn't. Something within the church community that they might run into is... "You can pray it away." I'm just being delicate here.

Patti: Oh no, trust me, you'd be shocked at how many people have said, well, if you had enough faith, you wouldn't be diabetic.

Emily: There you go.

Patti: Yes. That's spiritual abuse.

Emily: Yes, it is. Yeah, as a next-gen pastor, I am able to counsel the parents of our students. We have a handful of students that have been diagnosed or suspected of FASD. And because of this, I am able to educate them, as well as their parents, on FASD. I emphasize that FASD is a real diagnosis, even though you cannot see it, and that it's not just a "childhood brain thing," but it's a lifelong, full-body diagnosis. Another message someone may run into is that you're using it as an excuse, or it's not real; you're not trying hard enough. If you only did X, Y, or Z, it would all go away, or it'd all be better. And that's... maybe some of those people mean well when they say those things, but that's why it is so important to find someone like me or you. They have no idea how hurtful that is.

Patti: They have no clue that what we're talking about is a brain injury. Brain injuries don't go away. You can learn to adapt and make things that are challenging easier by learning how to add structures or workarounds - but they don't go away.

Emily: Yes, so find individuals that have walked that journey but who are walking in peace because they've figured stuff out already. There's a phrase that says, "You can't pour from an empty cup." So you can't go to someone who has an empty cup and expect your cup to be filled. So look for a person who can sit down, look you in the eyes, and offer you hope in a compelling and authentic way. Maybe sometimes we need correction, and that's okay if it's in a corrective, compelling, kind, compassionate, and understanding way. There's so much work for us to do, isn't there?

Patti: Absolutely. Oh my goodness, so much work to do. And is it any wonder I'm torn on how to prioritize what I need to be pursuing? Do I focus on training professionals? Well, yeah, because the more professionals out there that understand the neurobehavioral model, the more children and families will get real help instead of blame and shame. If more professionals understand behavior is biologically driven and not *choice*, it will limit all the damage that can happen if proper supports are never put into place; that leads to a lifetime of needless challenges because those children will be blamed and shamed and punished for biologically driven behavior until they finally find someone who gets neurodivergence. Do I focus on supporting parents for those same reasons? Do I focus on the adults who have never done the work to truly understand their differences? Or do I focus on advocacy? There's so much work for us to do. And I could easily be passionate about any one of those different directions. But isn't that the brilliant thing about trying to reach the 16.6+ million adults out there who have never really known the origin of their struggles? Once they figure it out, get that education, put those puzzle pieces together, and fine-tune their purpose, there will be many more people to help change the way in which the world looks at behavior.

Emily: Yes.

Patti: Because that's what it comes down to, is changing the way that behavior is perceived. It's not something to be pathologized and changed. It's something to be understood as a reflection of how the brain functions – no "behavior" happens without a multitude of underlying brain tasks, which are compromised by prenatal exposure to alcohol.

Emily: Again, we wouldn't ask someone that was blind to just try harder to see. Not being able to see could be a result of so many different things, but never the choice to not be able to see. And it's the same thing for adults with an FASD. It's not that you're choosing to have certain behaviors. Sometimes we have no choice over those behaviors. And again, so much of the literature is focused on FASD in childhood, but there's so much more to it than that. We must apply self-compassion and not beat ourselves up for not trying hard enough.

Patti: Yeah. I've been on this particular journey for five years, roughly, and I'm still putting puzzle pieces into place. I think, as with so many things in life, you don't get everything all at once because you can't handle everything all at once. You get things in bits and drabs as you're ready to incorporate that knowledge into life. For example, as a child, I thought the reason I was never accepted by my peers was that I was the only diabetic in school. Now I realize it's probably my FASD-driven quirks that made me just different enough to stand out. We all know kids can be cruel. Children who are neurodivergent are oftentimes are subject to bullying more than kids who aren't.

Emily: Within the autism community, the concept of masking is discussed frequently. I don't think it's discussed enough in the FASD community. You know, trying throughout childhood to not stand out, to not be identified as "different," (donning the mask of normalcy). Then by the time we became adults, we had mastered masking. Masking was survival.

Patti: We become a chameleon.

Emily: Yes. So I don't think we discuss it enough in the adult community of how exhausting that can be. And again, going back to the importance of community, in the adult FASD community, you can take that mask off, and people get you immediately. People aren't judging you. There's this sense of, "I can be myself and not worry about whether the mask falls off. I'm still accepted and, in fact, probably more accepted if I remove that mask." I think, too, something that complicates that is the fact that we're all impacted to such a variety of degrees.

Patti: True. Now some of us, the impact is minimal. You know, we function fairly well in life, and others of us are profoundly impacted. I think that confuses people who really have not heard about FASD, as well as those who are just learning about it. You know, there's that tendency to think, "Oh, I know someone who has this, so I know all about it." And you can do that with any diagnosis. But I think that's one of the things that's particularly confusing with FASD because it affects every aspect of our being. It truly is a whole-body diagnosis.

Emily: And within the spectrum, there are so many different diagnoses that add to the description. And then, you know, you've got people saying, this diagnosis (under the FASD umbrella) is low functioning versus this one is high functioning. But that's not how it works, either.

Patti: I know. Like this myth: FAS is the worst kind because it affects the face, so it's "full" FAS. All facial features mean is that alcohol was consumed on days 17 through 21 of the pregnancy. *That's all it means.*

Emily: And for me, I was diagnosed with full FAS. So that confuses people because they're like, "you don't look like it." I'm like, "Well if I showed you my baby picture, you might change your mind." But as we become adults, those features can change over time, and they can be less noticeable. So that confuses people. They've said to me, "Oh, you speak well." And I'm like, oh, my goodness. I'm pretty sure everyone that I know with an FASD speaks well.

Patti: (shaking her head) Emily, thank you so very much for your time and your wisdom. People just recognizing that prenatal alcohol exposure has touched their lives can very much benefit from what you have shared.

Professional and Personal Experiences
A Conversation with Kathryn Page

In this conversation, I speak with Dr. Kathryn Page, who has provided training, consultation, advocacy and support for those living with or supporting those living with FASD. Kathryn is the President of Northern California FASD. She has had a circuitous career, winding through starting and directing a FASD diagnostic clinic at the county hospital, working as a school psychologist, several years as a psychotherapist, and she is currently training the mental health clinicians of a large county in California on the subject of fetal alcohol spectrum disorders.

Patti: I have to say, Kathryn, I'm so curious about your story. Where does it begin for you?

Kathryn: Well, it has lots of beginnings, but let me get to the part about my direct connection with knowing about fetal alcohol—it happened by accident when I was visiting a friend in Seattle who worked at the hospital. She couldn't get together for lunch, so she said, "Why don't you go over to this grand round (lecture by doctors)? You know, give you something to do." The presenters were Ann Streissguth and Kierran O'Malley. At the time, my sixteen-year-old son, as he had been since he arrived in my household at the age of two months, was troubled, troubling and confusing. But my head exploded when I heard that grand rounds. He has a high IQ but no ability to use it. So watching the clinic the next day, it was very moving, and I was lit on fire. I went back to my work, which was with a small nonprofit working with kids with learning disabilities in groups, and I lobbied for us to open a diagnostic clinic.

Patti: Oh, wow. Let me interrupt for just one second. What is your professional background?

Kathryn: PhD in clinical psychology. I'm not licensed because I picked a fight with the board thirty-five years ago, and they won. I've done an internship at Stanford in psychiatry, completed my dissertation, got the degree; I just shot myself in the foot with the Board of Psychology. And yes, I can see the roots of fetal alcohol insofar as self-preservation not being my long suit. But I worked for many years in that field and gathered up a team at our county hospital. I was the director, and one day I come waltzing in with my new diagnosis of ADHD. The diagnosis explained a lot to me. It was a great relief. And one of our mentors was there. He and I had gotten to know each other really well and had become good friends. And I'm coming in with my ADHD diagnosis, and he just sort of looked at me funny and said, "You know, you're the diagnostician here. We've talked about your alcoholic mom. Put that together with your handwriting, your memory, and some other things about you... And, welcome to the club."

Patti: That's how he told you that you need to be looking at a FASD.

Kathryn: Oh, yeah.

Patti: So what is it about the handwriting? I don't know that one yet.

Kathryn: Poor hand-eye coordination. It's different for everybody. We're all different. From knowing your story, I know that you sew. Me? I would run the needle straight through my finger, and I believe I did a few times. But I also have significant memory issues. They called me an "absent-minded professor" when I was a little kid because I kept losing and forgetting stuff, even though I was supposed to be this brilliant child. Verbally, I was a brilliant child. But in a practical sense, I was not. So that was my introduction to FASD being a fit for me. But then, after that, the county got a new medical director, a squeaky, clean, fresh-out-of-medical-school guy; he did not believe that fetal alcohol was a thing. In 2001 he shut us down. We were only operational for a year and a half. So anyway, the town of Susanville wanted me to take over a little grant and see about starting a clinic there. So I did. I got a big SAMHSA grant. But the town was really aligned against the whole construct (of FASD). You know, it's a prison town; there are three prisons there. The way they see it is there are bad guys, and there are good guys and we were just making excuses for bad guys. I'm going to also push back a little bit with what I've come to really object to in our field. Just the black and whiteness, like, "Consequences don't work," and, "Talk therapy doesn't work." Well, it depends on the person. There are so many labels thrown onto people. I got them a lot before my diagnosis of ADHD, and I still do. The idea that I am a lazy person, a thoughtless person, and, in many ways, not the person that I wish I were. Some of these labels are not untruthful. They are not kind and not the most neurologically informed, but they are also not untrue.

Patti: Right.

Kathryn: And so, even though I can pick through to the neurological wiring that contributes to me not finishing things, or getting great ideas and not following through... I can find the neurology. I can name it. I can point to much of it in the brain. But that doesn't change the fact that it is also a bunch of stuff that I wish I didn't have in my makeup.

Patti: Yeah.

Kathryn: And so, your question (in an unrecorded initial conversation) about in what way does knowing that I have fetal alcohol affect how I care for myself and what I do... It does affect it in many ways. The main one is what we would wish for everybody involved with us—beginning with ourselves—to be able to transmit (to us)... and that is mercy—compassion, mercy, and understanding.

Patti: That's really grace. Grace truly is the equipping of someone to complete a task or to reach a goal.

Kathryn: And grace. And so that's a big one that I've really tried for a lot. Because as we know, we can't put the brain cells back that weren't there, but we can maximize the chances for self-regulation and support that will help us achieve what we want to achieve.

Patti: Right.

Kathryn: I will never have a better memory. I will never be good at planning. So the main thing under that mercy heading is knowing that it's okay to ask for help and who to ask for help from. That's really big, and that's one of the things that I push when I give trainings as a therapy goal. Also, self-advocacy and knowing your feelings — because there seems to be a little disconnect with many of us. It took me forever to learn to recognize my feelings. I knew it was a good idea. But it took therapists, and it took that big yellow chart with the smiley faces. It took a great deal of learning. Yeah. And I think, too, it was hard to know about other people's feelings. What might people be feeling in various situations? But it's another to…

Patti: Similar to the difference between sympathy and empathy. Sympathy is head knowledge, whereas empathy is the heart.

Kathryn: Right. So there does seem to be a disconnect that makes it possible for us to have sympathy if we're basically caring people. But the welling up of instantaneous fellow feeling. I don't have it. But I walk my way to putting myself into other people's shoes. I tell you, I think it's one of the reasons I was such a good therapist and still am. Because I have to ask people, "What does that feel like? Really? Oh, is it like this? Oh, no. Okay. Tell me more." Yeah. I'm really curious because I really didn't know. And so people were glad to have a chance to talk to somebody that was really, really interested."

Patti: Yes! That would enhance the quality of service any provider can give — to not assume we know what those whom we are helping feel at any given time.

Kathryn: So, back to your question about how I am managing this (my FASD) now? One of the things that I know is that I seem to need an enormous amount more rest than other people. I get exhausted. I have sensory stuff. I'm very sensitive to sounds and smells, and tastes, and I get worn out.

Patti: Sensory issues and fatigue. Two very common issues.

90

Kathryn: You're probably aware of the research that used functional MRI to compare those with and without prenatal alcohol exposure; doing a simple math task, I think it was. Everyone in the study could solve the problems. But the brain imagery showed how much more of the brain was recruited to solve the problems by people who had alcohol exposure than the people without. So there is tiredness and exhaustion. So what I do now is to walk that line between giving myself enough rest and indulging in what I do think is a kind of laziness – times like, "I don't know what to do exactly. It's a really warm day. I think I'll just go to sleep." Even when I'm not that tired, I think one of the things that has always plagued me, and plagues me still, is having an insubstantial sense of self. What I mean by that is that every day is a new day. Every day I write in my journal. What are my thoughts? What are my feelings? What are my impulses? Because if I don't write it down, I really don't have a sense of who I am. I don't have a sense of what's important. I don't have a sense of momentum; I don't. Every day, I start from scratch. Then I meditate and clear my chakras, which fires up energy. Then I pray. (At the age of seventy-three, I don't have to work anymore unless I want to.)

Patti: I never would have guessed that. Maybe sixties, because you have a little bit more gray hair than I do. But I never would have guessed seventy-three.

Kathryn: Oh, thanks. So that's living life effectively. I'm going to make sure that you know another piece of research. Okay. Cardiac orienting response.

Patti: I've never heard of that.

Kathryn: I think this is key research. You know how the (FASD) field has wanted to be able to diagnose or recognize FASD before the age of three, but we don't in the absence of abnormal facial features.

Patti: Right.

Kathryn: But the field is trying. So there was a study involving some infants prenatally exposed to alcohol and some not exposed. The researchers would shine a bright light or ring a loud bell near them. The babies had been fitted with electrodes for the purpose of watching their heart rates. They had two questions: 1) how intensely did the heart rate go up, and 2) how many repetitions did it take to habituate, for their little nervous systems to have learned that these stimuli were not cause for alarm.

Patti: Yes.

Kathryn: And it came out just as you would predict. So what we have is for those prenatally exposed to alcohol, we have biologically installed in us a greater upset-ability. We take things hard.

Patti: Boy, doesn't that explain the struggles of hundreds of kids on my caseload through the years. Oh, my goodness.

Kathryn: Yeah. And everybody's talking to kids or clients, like, "Could you just lighten up?" or "Let me teach you some breathing techniques." But instead, if there is sufficient cognitive capacity (in the client) and a sufficient (emotional) connection between clinician and kid... if the kid could come to a place where they get to know their own nervous system... For example, being able to reflect and say, "Oh yeah, there I go again. That's just my cardiac-orienting reaction. This will pass." To the extent that you can learn to do that, that would be a game changer! Yeah. But even with me, it is only a partial game changer. Because I can still respond to something that anybody else would let roll off their back. When I react, it's not outward. I react inside. Before I learned this, I just took it as more evidence that I was a weak and a bad person with no character at all. I thought I was self-absorbed and made mountains out of molehills. And God, do we have a lot of phrases to describe our glitch characteristics.

Patti: I'm wondering if that could be related to some of the sensory overstimulation.

Kathryn: Yes, it sure seems like it

Patti: When I was younger, I was a typical teen. I loved the shopping mall. I loved amusement parks. I loved discotheques. I drove my car with the sunroof open and the volume up. My husband works in the oil industry, so he's worked around loud machinery for decades. This has impacted his hearing, even with earplugs, and he tends to keep the volume up. I have found that the older I get, the more sensitive to noise I get. If we're in the pickup and he's got the volume up, I find myself trying to become part of the seat and to disappear because it feels like I am being physically assaulted. It's not just noise though, but all my sensory stimuli. I'm so much more sensitive now, sensory-avoidant, really, and I realize that this is because for whatever reason, my neuroception has changed to falsely cue me of danger.

Kathryn: I'm very distractible by everybody around me: their mood, their conversation, their facial expressions, their clothes. I cannot focus on a concert. I can't focus on a symphony. I can't focus on a play. It drives me nuts. I've tried ADHD meds, but it was too uncomfortable. And this brings up another bit of misinformation that drives me nuts. People say that if ADHD symptoms are from the FASD and not truly from ADHD, then the meds aren't going to work. That's wrong. They do work. It depends on the person; it varies. Up until very recently, nobody was sorting out who among the ADHD research subjects were exposed to alcohol vs not. So most of the research done on the effectiveness of ADHD meds was done on a "contaminated field." It was done on a bunch of people with prenatal alcohol exposure. No one knows what proportion.

Patti: Okay.

Kathryn: Now, if you have the DSM-version (the Diagnostic and Statistical Manual, a book of codes that allow insurance to be billed) of ADHD, it will say that if you have inattention, are hyper and are impulsive, and these symptoms interfere with your life, you're eligible for that diagnosis. If that's basically it, if you *don't* have any cognitive, adaptive, regulatory, sensory or issues with abstract concepts—even if you have prenatal exposure to alcohol, you don't have FASD, just a good solid case of ADHD, garden-variety... But if you have ADHD *and* you have a bunch of that other stuff, *and* there was alcohol, you probably have FASD. You'll still also qualify for a diagnosis of ADHD, and the meds may work on you. But what's being left out of that DSM discussion is the fact that all that research on those medications was done on people who did have FASD. It just wasn't called that. So yes, it does work for some people, and no, it doesn't work for others.

Patti: There's so much misinformation among our systems of care, whether it's mental health or the developmental agencies. People with FASD are so underserved because they may not have the cognitive capacity to make approaches traditionally utilized be effective on a consistent basis. I am so passionate about reaching other professionals — I want them to have better tools and a brain-based perspective, where behavior is viewed as being reflective of someone's ability to process information. But honestly, most of my work is in the coaching world.

Kathryn: Hmm.

Patti: You know, even if I can't get into systems of care, I can help families. I can help neurodivergent adults as people, like you and I, are discovering later in life that prenatal exposure to alcohol has contributed to making life kind of sucky at times.

Kathryn: So, who are your coaching clients now?

Patti: I have two coaching programs. One is for parents. You know, you can't work a quarter of a century in child welfare and not want to give your heart and soul to parents, birth, foster or adoptive, because they're raising the next generation. I would love to have a contract with my county to train biological parents. And also, the social workers who could benefit from knowing that maybe the parents on their caseloads are struggling with their case plan, not because they are lazy or uncaring or unmotivated, but because they don't have the cognitive capacity. My other coaching program is for adults. Perhaps they've been told that, for some reason, they are neurodivergent but have never methodically explored their challenges. Perhaps they've never realized they've been self-medicating with addictive substances or behaviors for more reasons than because they hated a parent or step-parent or it was more fun than staying in class. I wanted to ask you, though, about something you mentioned briefly a while ago in our conversation. You were talking about some of your struggles, and you spoke of having a fresh slate every morning. I'm curious what was it like to realize that those lifelong struggles could be explained by FASD?

Kathryn: It was an enormous relief and the source of the mercy that I give to myself. And even though I do still get into pretty gloomy thinking sometimes, really bordering on depression, and really unhappy with myself — even though I can explain it, I do not like how I function in many ways. But it *did* shift me over from thinking I am just a failure as a human being and all that self-condemnation over to acceptance. Explaining all this to friends is a challenge, and it's one that I don't think I will ever fully manage. Friends are often preoccupied with their own issues and don't think about how what they say to me comes across. Like the other day, when I was talking with a friend about visiting, they said, "Why don't you make the plan and let me know?" Then when I reminded her that plans aren't my strong suit, she said that it would be "good practice". I was so jolted by that because there are very few absolute safe zones. It was thoughtless and hurtful and would be like saying to someone who suffered from chronic depression that if they smiled more, it would be good practice for them. Getting a diagnosis gives us a way of wrapping our heads around our struggles. It provides a container that makes it easier for us to manage our feelings about various struggles.

Patti: Yes.

Kathryn: But when the whole rest of the world doesn't see that... For example, if I lose something or if I forget something, which happens all the time, even though I try so hard not to people's feelings get hurt, and they might think I just don't care. Or they'll be irritated—it's hard to keep in mind someone else's disabilities when those challenges are spotty, embedded in otherwise pretty functional behavior.

Patti: So one of the reasons I was so excited to talk with you, Kathryn, is because you, like myself, are both a professional in this field and have living experience with it. From our previous conversations, I know that we both have a lot of frustrations about systems of care not recognizing the prevalence of FASD and not recognizing that a different approach to help people thrive and live their best life is needed. So, I'm wondering what your thoughts are about that. I wanted to include this topic in particular because people who resonate with what all of us are saying are likely to face these frustrations when they seek help in their communities. So what might be some things that readers can arm themselves with to get the best possible access to care?

Kathryn: Oh. Boy, that's an interesting question. I have a kind of flippant answer to that.

Patti: Okay.

Kathryn: I'll just tell you what it is. It's to get a diagnosis and see if you can get the staff trained.

Patti: Okay. That's very similar to what my answer would be. So you and I both do staff development training. I have a very difficult time finding open doors to do that. Do you think consumers would have a better chance of opening that door for agency training by demanding it?

Kathryn: No. That's been tried and, I gather, only very occasionally successful. CASA is a good avenue, or a lawsuit hanging in the balance. Unfortunately, it just may take a handful of lawsuits.

Patti: Okay. So, this kind of leads to the topic of advocacy. Not only for our kids but for self-advocacy. Do you have any thoughts that the readers could benefit from for self-advocacy?

Kathryn: Oh yeah. First, I should say self-advocacy is at the heart of all the trainings I do for mental health professionals. Because self-advocacy really, in the best of all worlds, needs to be one of the main goals of therapy. And it will look different for each person. Developing a really fine skill at apology has to go right there, along with self-advocacy, because the stuff that we do can be irritating and aggravating, even if people do understand.

Patti: What can you say about pursuing a diagnosis in terms of resources or people? Few people are as fortunate as you were to be working arm-in-arm with FASD professionals. (smiles)

Kathryn: Well, I think two things. One, definitely call around. Two, you're probably not going to turn much up, if anything. So you're left probably with where most people are, families and individuals going on "as if."

Patti: Live life as if the diagnosis is in place. Okay. That's what I'm doing; when I already knew I had symptoms of it, effects of prenatal exposure, having my mother confirm that she drank daily was good enough for me.

Kathryn: But what I recommend using instead if you don't have a solid diagnosis is to use the language, "I have a brain injury. I have a brain injury (from before birth), and it affects my memory. It affects several things, but what I need from you (whoever you are speaking to) is to ask you the great favor of X, Y, or Z." (If memory is an issue, then adding), "I'm going to ask you to repeat this (whatever was said or explained) probably tomorrow when we meet again," or even, "What I'm really asking you is to try to keep in mind that I have a brain injury so that you don't get irritated with me." And just know that this oftentimes looks like thoughtlessness.

Patti: Yes.

Kathryn: Because it does. It looks like thoughtlessness.

Patti: That is so powerful. A brain injury prior to birth takes all the shame away.

Kathryn: That is, in fact, what it (FASD) is.

Patti: That is so powerful because a few of the other contributors to this book ended up going to pediatric geneticists for their diagnosis, even though they were adults. But had they not had infant pictures showing FAS, I don't know if they would have gotten a diagnosis at all. So for the rest of us, since most of us don't have the facial features, I really like that approach of saying, "I have a brain injury that has given me challenges in the following areas…"

Kathryn: Right, and you don't need to lay out the whole story to everybody.

Patti: I really, really like that. And that fits very well with the approach that I use in my Neurodiversity Mapping program, which methodically explores what are those struggles that someone has because it's different for each of us. Is it memory? Is it generalizing learning from one setting to another? So, I really, really like that. That is a gem.

Kathryn: Do you throw in the regulatory aspects?

Patti: Yes, especially when I work with parents of neurodivergent or FASD children.

Kathryn: There are things that I don't do because I'm just so damn triggered. I don't work with kids. I really cannot work with kids because I'm just triggered all over the place. I get upset. I get mad. I get impatient. A big part of self-advocacy, for me, is knowing where I'm not going to do a good job. So I just stay away. And if anybody asks me why, then I will explain it.

Patti: Yeah, I'm not a kid person either, so I find it very ironic that I have worked for the past quarter century in child welfare. But primarily, I work with the adults.

Kathryn: Right. Exactly. I work with the adults. I do think that's part of self-advocacy —to know where to put ourselves, where we can be most useful—and where not to. Even so, there are days where I'm just functioning really low. Sometimes I have to cancel an engagement because I know that, barring some miracle, I'm going to be, you know, I'm going to be just not all there.

Patti: That makes me think of living with and supporting my mother with her dementia. She clues me in very easily to when I am dysregulated and need to bring myself back into regulation. Because most of the time, I can let the behaviors from her brain injury just roll off my back like water off a duck. But other times, they're so irritating, and then I know that I need to step out and take care of myself so that I can support her.

Kathryn: I was thinking of maybe another aspect of self-advocacy as you were talking, which is that I have a few friends who tend to bend over backwards to accommodate my brain stuff, and sometimes it's way more than I need and becomes irritating. For instance, I have friends, some of whom are a little bossy to begin with, who tell me what to say. I know what to say to people, but they will direct me, "Just tell them A, B, and C." I don't know whether to attribute it to their personality and occupation or if they're being super cautious about the kind of support that I may need.

Patti: I have someone in my life that does that as well. Yes, it is extremely irritating.

Kathryn: And so another part of self-advocacy is really learning how to delicately set mutually respectful boundaries.

Patti: Yes. I think this is just such important information. Really, not just for those of us who have FASD, but for *everybody*.

Kathryn: Oh yes, I think so too. I think what's different about us, really, especially those of us who function normally or even a little higher than normally, in some ways, and who look totally normal, is the expectations. The appearance of normalcy leads to unrealistic expectations for us by others. Then, people can so easily feel disappointment or anger when we don't meet their expectations.

Patti: There are so many gems in this conversation – this has taken us right back to FASD being an *invisible* disability. Is there anything else, Kathryn, from your lived experience living with an FASD that you would want to share today?

Kathryn: I think one of the struggles for me that I may never fully overcome, although I'm a lot farther than I used to be, is acceptance. There can be much shame, disappointment and sorrow around not following through with intentions, either things I had wanted to do for myself or had promised to do for others, or not doing things to the level that I would like to. As a psychologist, I can untangle the neurological substrate and identify what the threads are and what the wiring is that got in the way… but the emotions are still there; I can talk myself down, but I will probably always have to.

Patti: Well, that just reinforces the reality that having a cognitive appreciation for all those aspects, is so very different from the emotional feelings.

Kathryn: I must say, to have a cognitive understanding is where it kind of has to start. But if there is a possibility of really good therapy that works on attachment issues and attachment patterns in relationships, and not just a cognitive-behavioral approach… having a therapist who's really willing to get in there and be in relationship with you is going to be necessary for healing. That's my great wish: that everybody could find that kind of therapy —and afford it.

Patti: We have so much work to do in this world, don't we?

Kathryn: Yes, we do. Good thing you're on the young side.

Patti: (laughs) As my husband counts the days till our retirements. Kathryn, thank you for joining me.

Adoption, Trauma, Mental Health & FASD
A conversation with Nury van Beers

In this conversation, I speak with Nury van Beers, author and advocate in the Netherlands. Nury shares her story of numerous adverse childhood experiences (ACES). Her resilience is a moving testimony that while life can be very messy, in many ways, we can take back the power and determine how we will live our lives. As of this writing, Nury has recently joined the International Adult Leadership Collaborative of the FASD Changemakers.

Patti: Hi, Nury. Thank you for joining me on this project. I'm really curious to learn more about your story.

Nury: Well, I always knew I was kind of different. I really struggled at school. I struggled at home with my sisters. I have two sisters, and I noticed I was different from them. My whole life, I tried to be popular, to belong, and to fit in. So that was my focus. How can I be like anybody else? I didn't think, "I am different." I just thought I am "wrong," I am "not good enough." I don't belong. I should change. I should do better. Then I met my husband in rehab, and I thought, "Wow, he is really different." But he made me very curious, and I wasn't judging him. I had been addicted to alcohol and drugs, and he had been addicted to gaming and medication. We began dating in rehab, but after a while, when we were out of rehab, we started to struggle in the relationship. So many things that he was struggling with I didn't accept in myself, so I wanted to change him. I wanted to make him better like I was trying to make myself better. But I couldn't. I really struggled with that. One day I was lying in bed, crying, praying, "Why can't I change this man? Why do we have so many problems? Why does he doesn't he understand that I just want to help him? Can you please give me an answer?" The answer I got from my higher power was to see my whole life in a different light. I saw how I was different from others. I saw things with Floris that I saw in myself. Then, as I was lying in bed, I thought, "Oh my God, I'm autistic," because that is his diagnosis, and if we're alike, then...

101

Patti: Nury, you just gave me chills. There's so much power in what you just said. The desire to fit in… kazillions of people out there in this world can relate to that desire to fit in and to that self-condemnation for not fitting in. But we're not meant to fit in someone else's box. I'm so glad that you came to that truth, but oh my gosh, can I relate to that! I was never popular growing up. Not until I had really made it all the way through college and was working is when I finally started to feel like people genuinely liked me. People saw my sense of humor. You know, sometimes there's an expression here in the States about a joke landing like a lead balloon. When I was young, all my jokes landed like lead balloons. But all of a sudden, you know, my jokes are funny. And people are laughing at them. I'm not sure what clicked or what changed. But that desire to fit in and to find people who will appreciate you for who you are is so strong.

Nury: I've had tons of therapy my whole life because I was diagnosed with a lot of things. In the beginning, it was Borderline Personality Disorder, ADHD and DID.

Patti: Dissociative Identity Disorder?

Nury: Yeah, I heard voices my whole life. I had 14 voices and alters. But I didn't switch; I was always at the steering wheel (in my head) if that makes sense. Sometimes I would listen to what they would say. I know that I was sexually abused when I was very, very small. In the rehab center where we were, there was a book published in the Netherlands, The FAS-Project. It had pictures of children and explained what fetal alcohol syndrome was. I remember looking at those pictures. I was very curious about it. A social worker at the rehab showed me an article about fetal alcohol syndrome because he knew I was adopted. He knew my (birth) mother was a prostitute. He knew that we were on the streets, so he said to me, "Maybe you should read this." He knew I had troubles. I sometimes went to my social workers there, questioning if I damaged my brain because I drank so much. My memory is often so poor - could I have Alzheimer's or Korsakoff Syndrome? They kept telling me, "No, you can't. It's just the stress." But I read the article.

Patti: Did you turn to alcohol to bury feelings of pain or anger or rejection?

Nury: Yeah, I was eleven years old when I started drinking. My birth mother was an alcoholic, and my adoptive mother in the Netherlands also drank a lot. She was living with a narcissistic man. She did what she could. She had a lot of stress. She was hiding her boxes of wine in the laundry basket. The first time (I snuck some of her wine) was because I was sexually abused by my neighbor. I couldn't tell anyone at home because they weren't (emotionally) available for me. I was ashamed. I thought it was my fault. So I didn't talk to anybody about it, and I started drinking. I was hooked from the beginning. I always hid it from my parents and my sisters. At some point, my father knew, but he just didn't care. I didn't have much support from my whole family. When they tried to help me, it wasn't in a way that benefited me. They were too strict and would complain, "Why can't you do this? Why are you weird?"

Patti: They were trying to put you in their box – their expectations of how things should work and what we should all be capable of doing.

Nury: They didn't know any better. I know that right now. I was very loyal to my sisters my whole life, but now I'm breaking that normative because I wasn't happy people-pleasing them anymore.

Patti: What has been their response to your saying, I am on the FASD spectrum.

Nury: Well, the response of one sister I never got because I didn't speak to her anymore after I got into therapy. I was thirty-three when I got into a trauma center to treat my traumas from sexual abuse.

Patti: Good for you to take that step. That is very courageous. To purposely go somewhere and rip the scab off.

Nury: Yeah, I really needed to because I was struggling at home in my marriage. I got aggressive at times. I wasn't suicidal; I've never really been suicidal because I was afraid to do that. I always wanted to be a mother, but I figured I couldn't be a mother if I had this trauma, so I had to do something about it.

Patti: That's a very strong motivation, isn't it?

Nury: When I went there, things got weird with my sisters and me. Suddenly my one sister wouldn't speak to me anymore. I don't know why that was, but I can say that things got different between us. It's still a mystery to me, but our relationship can't go back to what it had been.

Patti: When we learn something that shakes up our world to the extent that dealing with the trauma does or getting an FASD diagnosis, you can't unlearn those things, and there is no going back. What about your other sister?

Nury: My other sister and I had a history of cycling between getting along and then fighting. A few years after I was in the trauma center, when I was free of my PTSD, my other sister and I found that we were both pregnant at the same time. She was due (to deliver) one week before me. So we decided that we should try again. I felt it was a gift from God because I was writing a book, my first book, about fetal alcohol syndrome and becoming a mother. My sister was older than me and had more memories of our life in Colombia. In the past, she arranged a meeting on Skype, so I met my birth mother. That was awkward. We have a brother and two more sisters who are still in Colombia. My sister never felt at home with our (adoptive) parents in the Netherlands. She was always looking for our birth family. She found them, I think, through Facebook. She went there on vacation. I don't really know the story, but she found them eventually. I was at the rehab center at the time, thank God, because I would have relapsed had I been at home.

Patti: I'm glad you had that support.

Nury: Yeah, me too. This happened about the same time that my adoptive mother had a stroke, which left her unable to talk anymore and paralyzed on one side. I was in rehab when that happened as well. My sisters and I became very close because of that for a while. We kind of pulled each other through, so to say. And a couple of weeks later, she found our birth mother. I was very angry about that because I always felt rejected by her. I had been angry at my birth mother my whole life because I had a shit life here in the

Netherlands with my narcissistic dad and my mother, who is unaware of everything, and that's all because of my birth mother. I always knew she drank, but…

Patti: You never connected that to the possibility that you had FASD.

Nury: No, I didn't make that connection until later. I think making the connection at that time would have been too much. I ended up relapsing, I think, because of all of the bad news I was receiving so close together. But I've been sober now for ten years.

Patti: Yay! Congratulations.

Nury: Yeah, I'm very happy about it. Anyway, about the time my sister and I had our babies, my sister asked me if I knew our mother was coming to the Netherlands for a visit. I was shocked. My whole life, I had been angry at her, but once I became a mother myself, I didn't want to be angry anymore with my mother. I wanted to give my daughter a grandmother, and for my daughter to meet her. *I* wanted to meet my mother. I was open to it. So I decided to forgive her, just like that. That's when I told my sister that I have Fetal Alcohol Syndrome. In the beginning, she looked at the traits we have in common – forgetfulness, being a bit chaotic, and said she must also have them. But then she viewed it as an "excuse" for not wanting to work hard in life, and since she was a hard worker, then she couldn't have it, and therefore I didn't either.

Patti: I can relate. One of my brothers is willing to consider prenatal exposure as possibly underlying some of his struggles in life, but the other questions if it's a copout and if I'm blaming our mother for the areas of life where I have struggled. But, as you know, it's not about wanting to shift blame; it's about the freedom that comes with understanding things in the right context. It's not about having an excuse for not living up to other people's expectations. It's not about that at all, but knowing what our struggles are enables us to put workarounds in place, accommodations.

Nury: Yeah. I feel like for my sisters, it's difficult to see because they just see me not struggling (to meet goals), not working, and not doing my best. They were confused because they saw me as being very smart and one of my sisters would come to me for advice on emotional issues, so they couldn't see how I could have FASD. When I had been drinking, I could be mean. Not that I intended to hurt them, but I did. I can understand why they thought I had those intentions. I used to lie a lot also – they always assumed it was because I wanted attention.

Patti: One of the things that many of us with FASD do is called confabulation. And that has to do with our memory. To others, it looks like lying. But it's not lying because there's no intent to deceive. We're just trying to explain things we lack memory for.

Nury: Yeah, I would say things out of trying to fit in, and then the next day, I would tell another story. People were like, "Okay, she's crazy." I was mad at my sister when she (brought that up and) said that it (FASD) is an excuse. She later apologized, and we both admitted that we had both changed a lot over the years.

Patti: That's something that we see all the time when someone has a "dysfunctional lifestyle" for whatever reason; their whole family gets so used to those dynamics so that when someone quits drinking or quits doing whatever it is that they've been doing, the family has a lot of resistance. Changing the way you relate to people takes work, and sometimes the status quo feels easier.

Nury: I was warned of that by a lot of people in recovery. Yeah, so we tried in the beginning, but that doesn't make it any easier when things don't work out. Two people in the same relationship can have very different experiences; what can be okay for one may cause PTSD in the other person. That's what happened to me. I have a brain that doesn't work so well under stress. And it is very hard for me to handle anyone's lack of consistency in their attitudes and actions.

Patti: Nury, your challenge may predate any of the conflicts you've had with your sisters or anyone else. Did you not say that the mom who gave you life was for a time in prostitution?

Nury: Yeah.

Patti: Yeah. So that world is so full of danger, and women in that world are in situations where anything could go wrong at any moment. There are, therefore, high levels of stress hormones, Cortisol, flowing through her body. So if she had high-stress levels throughout her pregnancy with you, that has its own effects on you and not being able to regulate your stress because what happens is it literally breaks the baby's emotional thermostat.

Nury: That's a really good point. You know, one of the untrue things being said about FAS here in the Netherlands is that people with FAS don't have a conscience. That makes me angry. For a long time, that made me think that I did *not* have FAS because I am always thinking of other people. I am independent as hell. I always think before I do something, so I can't have that (FAS).

Patti: There are a lot of things that you can read in articles or online that are based on either misinformation or myths or that are based on research that is done with a very small sector of the population. So if we conflate the results of a study and generalize it to all people on the spectrum, we're going to make a lot of mistakes like that. So what has it been like looking back through your life and realizing that probably the FASD explains much of your struggles? Like never fitting in, which we talked about. That's something that many of us struggle with for whatever reason. Just the nature of feeling "different," especially when we're kids because kids are so often cruel to each other. They don't like differences. Were there some other pieces that were really surprising for you when you realized, "Oh, this must be the FAS?"

Nury: Well, for me, a big part was the social awkwardness. But I always try to fit in, and I'm very good at hiding, kind of acting my way through situations, mirroring people. Drinking helped me be social but left me so tired. I've learned how to be social without drinking, but I don't have many friends, and I like it this way. Sometimes I'm lonely, I miss having a deep friend, you know, someone you can really talk to, that knows you, that calls you whenever, My husband is my best friend now. I wasn't myself for a long time, not drinking. But now I'm kind of getting used to myself, and I like being on my own. I like that.

Patti: Are you falling in love with yourself? You know what I mean? Discovering who you really are? Having peeled away all those other pieces?

Nury: I am. I am like my own best friend; I can say that. I rely on myself, and I follow my intuition, which I'm very grateful for. I am true to myself, I really have my conscience, and I think about things. I'm trying to live my life with integrity. I like talking to myself better than anybody else.

Patti: You said earlier that you've written your first book. How many books have you authored?

Nury: Just the one.

Patti: Are you working on another one, or have dreams to write another book?

Nury: No, not at the moment. It was very hard to do, but also because I was pregnant and in the early months after giving birth. It was my story of living with FASD to advise social workers about how they can help us and how they should see us.

Patti: Oh, wonderful. I hope that you can get that translated from Dutch to English so that you can get a worldwide audience!

Nury: Yeah, writing the book was the second thing that I did after learning I had FAS. Before that, I was researching online about motherhood for those of us with FAS. I went on a forum, and I wrote to other mothers anonymously. Does anyone here have fetal alcohol syndrome? Are you a mother, and how do you do that? I want to know, what are your struggles? Because I was researching how to be the best mother I could be.

Patti: I just saw a post like that on FLYING WITH BROKEN WINGS today.

Nury: The post comes up a lot. But in the Netherlands, on this forum, it wasn't for people with fetal alcohol syndrome, it was just a random forum. All the women were very mean, and they said that I should be sterilized, I didn't know what I was doing, I was being selfish. I got that reaction from so many people. Then I was so scared and so hurt. I struggled with that for a very long time. But it also made me realize I really needed to go to therapy because those responses triggered me. Then on that same forum was a post from a magazine asking if they could interview someone with FAS. I said to interview me because I wanted to have my "coming out" as a way of overcoming what I experienced on that forum. And I was proud to tell my story.

Patti: How did that go?

Nury: Really well. And that article was my coming out to the rest of the world, including to my family and my sisters. I had known for a while, but I kept it (my FAS) a secret because I was afraid of what they would think of me - because that means saying publicly that our mother drank, and I was very scared of their reaction.

Patti: It really does feel like "coming out," doesn't it? There's tremendous stigma. But we didn't do this to ourselves.

Nury: I was also afraid to talk about it because I was afraid that the child services would come and take my daughter. I was very scared of that, and I still am.

Patti: Having FAS means that you have had a brain injury. There's nothing contagious about it. There's nothing that automatically means that you would in any way be an unfit mother. To make that assumption would be absolutely ludicrous! But I understand your fear. I was just reading a post today about someone being told by a social worker that they may have their child removed at birth because they have FAS. That just makes me so angry!

Having worked in child welfare for twenty-three years, it drives me batty when social workers say things like that out of their ignorance!

Nury: There is so much stigma around parenting and mental health and around FASD. The movie *I am Sam* really helps me (fight that fear). Writing my book did as well. I was very open in my book about my sexual abuse, about how it was in the family, everything. Yeah, and I plan on remaining open and honest. That's why I'm open here with you.

Patti: That's why you joined the International Adult Leadership Committee of the FASD Changemakers.

Nury: Yes.

Patti: Nury, you are such a brave young woman.

Nury: Thank you.

Patti: I can just see that you are going to make a difference in your corner of the world.

Nury: I hope so because, in the Netherlands, people don't want to talk about FASD. It's being talked about where it needs to be. It's like they don't want to bother other people with it.

Patti: Well, they don't want to talk about it in the US either. But this isn't a small problem. This is a worldwide problem. It's a universal issue, a health issue, as well as a developmental issue. The ramifications of prenatal exposure to alcohol are across every aspect of life and in every society. In so many ways, we've been struggling with this as long as we've had alcohol. There's nothing new about it, except the fact that we now have a diagnostic label, thanks to Dr. Jones discovering that it's a thing in 1973.

Nury: Yes, it's an ancient problem. Maybe I'm making big dreams, but if we can, we need to help the world fix it. I don't know that we can get rid of

FASD because there's alcoholism and sexual abuse, and there's so many reasons why a woman drinks during pregnancy. I don't think it will be entirely preventable. But at least when we know how to diagnose it and how to help people, I think we can avoid so many problems.

Patti: My second career choice was nursing. I remember being so surprised to learn that one-third of women continue to have periods throughout the first trimester of their pregnancy. So if you're still having cycles, why would you stop drinking?

Nury: Yeah, I never thought of that.

Patti: So we truly cannot judge women for drinking during pregnancy because, number one, they might not know (they're pregnant), and number two, the only way to avoid that possibility is to say, "You cannot have alcohol from the minute you start having a menstrual cycles until menopause is complete." And *that's* not realistic.

Nury: I don't think you can judge the women who drink because they are dependent upon alcohol. I know how difficult it is when you're addicted. Everything is just difficult. I met so many addicted women through the meetings, and I understand. I met a mother who has children with fetal alcohol syndrome also in the meetings. I'm not sitting in judgement over her. I'm not angry at her. I try to help her. I try to keep open conversation with her. But when you try to talk with them (about FASD), people get defensive and say alcohol is legal.

Patti: So, is there anything else that you would want people to know as they are maybe recognizing part of their journey through the story you shared and through our conversation that might encourage them?

Nury: Well, I think that people are afraid to get the diagnosis or afraid to tell what's wrong with them. But I really feel that you should be true to yourself. So, if you feel that at this point, there is something wrong with you, but you're not open to exploring it, don't. There is time for everything in your life. I just want to encourage people to *be curious* at all times, and when they see something like, oh, that's too difficult, maybe let it go. You know, for me, it was very difficult. I had to do everything step by step and not everything at a time because if I would do that, I would relapse. I would maybe get suicidal and more depressed. But when you're *curious*, there's safety in that. And know your triggers. Know when it is safe to explore this topic and when it is not – maybe more support is needed. So I'm very happy that you are doing this work. In facing this, you're very vulnerable but also very strong. Yeah, yeah. Vulnerable and strong at the same time. Use your strengths, but also listen to your limits.

Patti: Yes Nury, there's so much wisdom in those last two pieces that you said. There's so much there. By abiding by those two things, anybody's life would improve.

Nury: When we have a brain that is more like a child, you don't have to be so hard on yourself. I was hard on myself my whole life; I regret that

Patti: Remember that none of us knew what we didn't know until we finally learned it. So it doesn't do any good to beat ourselves up. We didn't know until we finally learned it. And the same thing for the people in our lives - the people who have trouble adjusting to the reality that we have an FASD. None of us knew until we figured it out. I'm so appreciative of our conversation and your openness to share your story, both the struggles and the victories. How far you have come! Ten years sober. A growing family.

Nury: I like doing things like this because I like to help. I'm a mother. I don't have a job. I like to participate anywhere I can.

Patti: I'm excited for your becoming part of the International Adult Leadership Committee of the FASD Changemakers, and I can't wait to see where that leads you! And I am excited about your book hopefully being translated into English so that it can go worldwide!

Triumphant Tales
A Conversation with Jessica Birch

In this conversation, I speak with Jessica Birch, who lives in Australia. Jessica's is a remarkable story of resiliency. Jessica is an advisory group member for NOFASD and for FASDHUB, Australia's national FASD organizations. She is a guest speaker at the University of Western Australia in the postgraduate course for the assessment and diagnosis of FASD. Jessica is a member of the International Adult Leadership Collaborative of the FASD Changemakers. She has campaigned alongside the Foundation for Alcohol Research and Education and has been part of an advisory group for the University of Queensland as well as the University of Sydney, with different clinicians and researchers there. She has also given a number of webinars and guested on several podcasts.

Patti: Hi Jessica, thank you so much for joining me on this project. We both know there are millions of people out there who have no clue that they're on the same journey that you and I are on. I'm really curious about your story. So just dive on in - tell me what your struggles have been and what got you thinking about FASD.

Jessica: Thank you so much, Patti, for including me in your book. My journey to diagnosis was not straightforward at all. I was officially diagnosed four years ago at the age of thirty-three... And that came on the back of a lengthy health battle throughout my twenties. But I thought I would just start by saying I was exposed to alcohol prenatally because my mother didn't know that she was pregnant. I was born in 1986, and at that time, there was very little information for new mothers about prenatal alcohol use during pregnancy. Shockingly, my understanding is that hospitals in the 80s were still giving women alcohol drips to stave off labor, so hospital procedures were actually causing developmental damage as well.

Patti: Just like when they used to use Thalidomide to combat morning sickness, but it caused horrendous birth defects.

113

Jessica: Yes, exactly. My mother was on a contraceptive pill when she fell pregnant with me. As soon as she found out she was pregnant, she stopped drinking. Unfortunately, the damage was done, and I had been exposed to varying levels of alcohol throughout the first trimester.

Patti: But you know what? It's not uncommon for women not to know they are pregnant. When I was in nursing school in the early 1980s, I learned that as many as one-third of women have no clue until they're in their second trimester because they still keep getting their periods.

Jessica: Absolutely. Mum didn't think that it was possible for her to get pregnant at that time. But we know now that is simply not the case…

Patti: Absolutely. But that's not uncommon either because there is no 100% effective method of contraception.

Jessica: I think it's so important for women to understand that if you are unsure of your contraception, you must be aware of consumption. I was in distress when I was born. They suspected I had meningitis, and it was quite a traumatic, very rough experience for my mum. But after some time in the NICU, she took me home. As a child, I had some quirks.

Patti: I call them quirks too.

Jessica: It really seemed, for the most part, that I was a smart, engaged kid, and I met my milestones. But there were definitely quirks…I had issues with my sleep, hand-eye coordination, gross motor skills, and sensory sensitivities. I was a bit slow being able to throw and catch a ball or knowing my left from my right. At 37 years old, I still struggle with my left and right. I feel like I've caught up quite a bit, but that was big for me as a child. Attention and focus were definitely an issue… I would daydream a lot, wouldn't be able to follow long instructions… But the other thing that I can say about me from around the age of four onwards is that I really struggled with my adaptive functioning, and I definitely didn't feel like I fit in or could make friends and keep them easily. And I always felt, even as a young child, kind of on the periphery of things. I remember being quite scared of my peers. I was much more comfortable with children that were quite a bit younger than me. Or they were quite a bit older than me.

Patti: Hmm, but we know that's so common.

Jessica: Yes, it's very common. But at the time, there was no context for understanding why. My mum could see that I wasn't really connecting with the kids that I should be connecting with. I was always gravitating towards younger kids. Looking back, we know that I was obviously struggling with my adaptive functioning... I became a very anxious and often lonely kid (and adult). I started to feel "less-than" very early in my life because I could feel I wasn't being accepted. I worked exceptionally hard to keep up with my peer group but often failed.

I became very adept at masking and hiding what I did not understand because I was desperate to be accepted... truly desperate. All I wanted was for kids to like me.

Patti: The younger kids were your age mates developmentally.

Jessica: Right. I have a normal IQ, but my adaptive, affective, academic and executive functioning have been deeply impacted. Not to mention, sensory and auditory processing issues and interoception. My nervous system is damaged, and there are many symptoms there too... Again, in hindsight, it was so obvious, but when you don't have the information to connect the dots, you don't have the context to put that in. The quirks are always chalked up as something else... it's interpreted as the child's personality, t's not seen as brain-based behavior that needs to be supported. Because I was seen as bright, brain injury was never considered, despite my mum inquiring with specialists throughout my life.

Patti: So, let me ask you: sensory issues.

Jessica: Oh my goodness, haha! I have so many sensory sensitivities. I'm both sensory-seeking and avoidant. I compulsively touch what I like. I'm obsessed with different textures. When I was a kid, I went through a phase where I could not stand being dirty or having a mark on me... If there was a drop of water on my shirt, I would rip off my clothes and ask for a new outfit. I couldn't let it dry and disappear, I had to change, or I would throw a tantrum. It would drive my mum crazy! I couldn't have my food touch or be mixed together, and I don't like people eating off my plate because they mess up the order in which I will eat the food. I'm very good at masking my upset when people mess with my food... but I definitely don't like it.

I'm very sensitive to light and started developing migraines as I got older. I now wear therapeutic glasses all the time to protect myself from headaches and fatigue.

I have a weak startle reflex and am very sensitive to loud or sudden noise. I can't handle too many competing sounds before I get really overwhelmed. My environment is always very clean, and I make sure I have a place for everything... I really struggle to think clearly if my environment is messy. I don't like being splashed, rained on, or slimy things... honestly, the list goes on and on...

I also have auditory processing issues and issues with interoception. I can see how badly my nervous system has been affected. In school, I would just conk out. Besides all the cognitive overload that was happening, there was just too much sensory input that was overloading me as well. Most people don't understand how hard people with FASD work just to be in the room and what the blowouts and recovery looks like. It can take me days and days to recover from sensory overload.

Patti: As a teen, I could handle large crowds and noisy environments, especially when I would go to the disco. But the older I get, the less tolerant of those environments I am.

Jessica: If I'm in a big crowd and I'm constantly getting knocked around, I get angry. I can't regulate my emotions. Yeah. I'm really sensitive to being knocked, shaken, or jostled around, I didn't like it as a kid, but I'm also much more sensitive to it now.

Patti: That's common too.

Jessica: So now, when I go into a supermarket, I'm hyper-aware of how I was feeling before going to the store and how I'm feeling after. So to be able to get through an active day, whether it was at school, with my family, or doing an activity, as soon as I came home from a situation where I had to engage and be "on", I'm completely exhausted, I conk out, you can't ask anything of me if I've hit my limit... I will just flip out. As a kid, I would sit in front of the TV for the entire night and zone out because I was actually completely overstimulated, and the only way I knew to wind down was to watch a screen, not having to think, not having to do, not having to move... And I still do that to this day; I still calm my nervous system like that.

Patti: That's really interesting because, as I was saying that I'm less tolerant of noise. I remember when I was a teenager, during the first couple of years I was driving, I loved blasting the radio in the car, like a typical teen. But now it is physically painful. It is *physically painful*. I feel like I'm being assaulted. Yes. By music.

Jessica: Oh my god. Yes, it is like that. I have tinnitus.

Patti: I do too. I've had it in my right ear for, like, I don't know, almost twenty years.

Jessica: I have quite intense tinnitus, and I'm very sensitive to loud and sharp noises. It is physically painful.

Patti: Yeah. So my husband works in the oil fields. So he's had some nerve damage to his ears. So he keeps the volume way up. We'll be driving down the street, and when the radio is up to my husband's liking, I press my back and my legs into the seat, willing myself to disappear. It's too much.

Jessica: I also can't deal with competing sounds.

Patti: Me neither.

Jessica: My attention, and ability to focus, coupled with auditory processing issues, make it difficult... I've got ADD symptoms, so if I have a lot of competing sounds, it's so hard to focus on one thing. And if I do it, if I am able to successfully focus on one thing while there are all these competing sounds happening, and engage and respond appropriately, the amount of fatigue is extreme! For example, I had a health assistant who was doing graded exercise therapy with me. One day, I was doing a session, and I said to her, "I'm so exhausted. I'm so over-extended that I canceled my driving lesson after your visit today because I just need a rest." She's not FASD-informed, and her response was, "Oh? I'm surprised by that. Why wouldn't you cancel our session instead of the driving lesson?" Although I do have to be careful with my exercise in regards to fatigue, I needed to explain to her that it is much easier for me to do a physical workout than it is to try to focus and concentrate on all the aspects of driving a car. There's so much risk management, making decisions and predictions, sensory overload, not to mention the multi-tasking, manoeuvring of the car, and all of the cognitive effort that goes into driving. Driving the car is exceptionally more exhausting than it is to do some exercise.

Patti: Absolutely. I'm just supposing that she's neurotypical and completely takes for granted all the things that her brain does to drive a car. I never took physics, but my brain knows how to compute physics when I'm driving: to judge speed, to judge stopping distance, to judge the speed of oncoming traffic, especially if I'm trying to pass on a two-lane road, paying attention to all the different gauges, all the other vehicles. Heaven forbid if you add the complexities of driving a stick shift! (laughs)

Jessica: Physical and cognitive fatigue is a huge issue for me. Trying to find the balance and pace myself is an ongoing battle, as with many people with FASD, I deal with multiple diagnoses. Before my FASD diagnosis, I was diagnosed with Postural Orthostatic Tachycardia Syndrome (POTS) as well as Myalgic Encephalomyelitis or Chronic Fatigue Syndrome (ME/CFS)...all these conditions are considered "hidden" and heavily stigmatized...you get labeled as lazy or unfocused... honestly, I had to do so much therapy around the word lazy, and I'm quite triggered if someone suggests I'm lazy because it's not my character. It's my disability.

Patti: I know, that makes me so angry. People with autoimmune disorders face stigma because no one can "see" their disabilities or point the finger at a cause to blame it on. So the person suffering from it gets blamed or disbelieved.

Jessica: It's been a hard battle, I must admit. I try to advocate and empower people who are confused about symptoms they are experiencing that could be neurological in nature.

I encourage them to stand up for themselves with health professionals and within the healthcare system. The amount of gaslighting, dismissals, snobbery, and diminishing of serious symptoms that I experienced throughout my journey to diagnosis and the battles that you go through with the public healthcare system here in Australia made me very, very ill and essentially prolonged unnecessary suffering… I'm definitely someone who went through that, and I had a lot of support (I needed it). Now I'm part of several advocacy and project groups for FASD, and I speak to a lot of parents and carers about my experience growing up without diagnosis. I was not a child with extremely violent behavior. I didn't punch things. I didn't kick holes in walls. I was a child that was very moody and would become withdrawn. I was short on patience and could get agitated quite quickly. If I didn't understand something that was being explained to me, I would get really, really angry, and I would have screaming meltdowns; Mum was caught the brunt of it, usually because she was trying to explain my math homework, and I just couldn't cope. I would try to understand, but if it wasn't explained exactly how I needed to be explained, I would just hit a wall. If someone kept trying to explain whatever it was that I wasn't grasping. I would flip out. But I wasn't violent. My mom's concerns were never seriously considered, and no health professional ever asked her about prenatal alcohol exposure. So when my mom was taking me to the specialists telling the doctors about issues, they would tell her that my behaviors were a phase and I "would grow out of them." But of course, I didn't grow out of the behaviors; they either got worse, changed, or sort of amalgamated into different things.

My mum, in so many ways, naturally accommodated my needs. If FASD had been more recognized, then there could have been more interventions, and I could have really avoided a lot of hardship, pain, and mental health issues as I got older. But I was very, very well loved and well supported in the ways that my mom knew how to support me.

Patti: I think my mom was a lot the same way. And I owe her my life. Leading up to my Type 1 Diabetes diagnosis, the pediatrician kept dismissing her concerns, calling her a worry-wart. But if she had not pestered him so much that he caved in and saw me… he told her I would have died by the next day. With FASD, often times kids and adults are given partial diagnoses – if the symptoms fit something more commonly diagnosed, doctors feel that's good enough to access services. But truly, it's not… It's this *and FASD*.

Jessica: Absolutely. My mom knew that her child was not going to do well if she didn't get a lot of sleep or if my blood sugar got low. She knew I had to have things labeled and organized, and clean. She had labels all over the house, and I think that really regulated me; we had a routine, and we did the same things on the same days. I think that protected me a lot in my younger years. Despite a supportive and loving home life, I was an inexplicably sad and lonely kid. Regardless of all my mom's efforts to help me socialize, I didn't integrate well. She was a single, working mom. She couldn't be there all the time to do an activity with me, which is what I always wanted, as I was too shy around other kids… I just wanted to do things with people I was safe with. Mum was always encouraging me to try new things; dance classes, art classes, surf lifesaving, girl scouts, and all sorts of things. I desperately wanted to do all those things as a child, but anxiety and fear of failure were very strong in me. I didn't integrate well. And I started internalizing very early on that I wasn't good enough or that I would fail at the task… that I was "different," and so I wouldn't try. I missed out on a lot because of that…

Patti: I always had that sense too, but I chalked it up to my diabetes as the reason why.

Jessica: I chalked it up to being mixed race. I was the only mixed-race child in my primary school.

Patti: And I was the only diabetic. I tried ballet in elementary school, but I could not stand the instructor. Oh, I couldn't stand her. And I would complain and complain and complain. Finally, my mom decided she was going to come and observe. And as we left that night, she said, "I should have listened to you. You don't have to go back again." The same thing happened with the Girl Scouts. I could not stand the one leader. The other one was okay. A lot of the other kids loved her, though. My sense now in looking back to understand what caused my strong reaction to these two women is that they were likely neurotypical, and so they didn't get me or work with me. I think, on some level back then, I knew it. I felt very unsupported by them. So that's what I was reacting to.

Jessica: That is so interesting that you say that because I have really similar experiences. In high school as well, but particularly in my primary school years, when they do a lot of peer group activities. I was terrible at sports; I had undiagnosed tachycardia but got a bit of flak for never wanting to participate. I don't do so well in team environments. I could struggle to understand the rules or objectives and what each person's role on the team was. That made it really hard to actually participate. So I got teased that I was "unfit" or that I was this, that, or the other thing. I was also uncoordinated, but if you think gross motor skills are a problem, add in tachycardia and fatigue. That's a problem for a little kid.

Patti: I joined the swim team one year because I love swimming. They expect you to swim each lap at full speed. And it would drop my sugar levels every time. So I'd swim at most two laps. And then I'd have to sit out. I never went to a meet.

Jessica: I feel like I'm a naturally social person. I desire to be social. I desperately wanted to be part of the group. I want to try all the new things. But having unrecognized, undiagnosed FASD is the complete antithesis to that. I remember when I was nine and ten years old, feeling like the teachers had it in for me. I was sort of placed in this group of popular girls. These girls were not only popular, but they excelled in school and their extracurricular activities, they were the girls that were chosen by the teachers to be school leaders in different ways, and they were all chosen for some important role or some responsibility but the teachers would leave me out. I sat on the periphery of this group and was often bullied within that group… The teachers seemed to have very little forethought of what that might do to a nine-year-old… watching every member of their peer group being chosen and you left out.

Patti: Me too.

Jessica: I was a part of the "cool kids", but I wasn't a cool kid, you know? They were the peer leaders, the sport team leaders, the dance troupe leaders, etc... I felt this dichotomy, I guess. Like, there was one part of me that felt that I was the same as everybody else, questioning why I shouldn't be chosen and be seen as one of the school leaders. And then there was this other side of me that felt completely unworthy and had this sense of knowing I wouldn't be chosen because "obviously" I wasn't smart enough and I wasn't liked enough. I just wasn't enough. I felt incredibly alone and unaccepted, yet I was always striving for acceptance. The teachers always separated me from the girls that I felt most comfortable with, and I couldn't understand why that was happening. I couldn't understand why all the girls in this group were chosen to be leaders of the school, but I wasn't chosen. I couldn't understand why they were all excelling in things, and I couldn't excel, even at school camps. At camp, we gravitated into groups of our choosing, but they separated me and put me in another camp. Even at nine years old, I felt completely "othered."

Patti: And that perpetuates the "othering." I'm curious how would you interpret it now?

Jessica: I still interpret it as being "othered." I mean, I feel the teachers assessed my capacity, with limited knowledge, didn't support me, and so I was relegated. It happened in high school too. Another thing that happened a couple of times is that when they were going to separate us into groups, we were asked to put on a piece of paper who we wanted our partner to be, fold up the piece of paper, and then they would make the groups based on what the children had asked for, as best they could. I would always pick the same kids, but I would never end up being put in those groups. In hindsight, I realized that what was happening is the kids I chose were not choosing me. When I realized that these kids, the people that I sit with at lunch, weren't picking me to be in their group, and the teachers weren't picking me either, that's when I really started internalizing the belief that I was completely unlikeable. Why didn't anyone like me? So from a very early age, I had a very deep sense of not being good enough, of not being accepted, and that there was something wrong with me. But I had no context, or awareness, or understanding for me to be able to pinpoint what was different about me.

Patti: How could you at nine years old? I think I skipped that because, in my family, there was such a high value upon learning and intellect, and intellectual achievement that I just became very defiant when I faced chronic rejection. I just turned it around and said, "They're into all this stupid stuff. I'm not going to waste my time with dolls!" So I threw myself into classes. When I got to high school, I took English classes as an elective.

Jessica: You know what's funny is that English was one of my favorite subjects. When I hit high school, I was good at English. I was good with words. And I took advanced English, and that's what I enjoyed, as well as history. I wanted to be one of the smart kids. I was told I was smart and capable, and I cared a great deal about being smart and capable. I have always been a crazy high achiever, but the best of me was never going to come out in the typical school environment. It was just too hard. I couldn't understand why I wasn't achieving the results that were expected of me and that I expected of myself.

For me, there was no defiance. There was just a lot of defeat, confusion, and dejection. I was just a sad little kid who turned into a sad teenager, who turned into a sad adult. My mom did everything in her power to make sure that I was happy, healthy, and well looked after and that I had all the opportunities I wanted, but I didn't throw myself into classes because I was scared. I became scared of them, and I became scared of failure. I became scared of people watching me. The anxiety and fear were quite strong in me. And I think that, too, is heightened when our neurodiversity is not recognized.

Patti: We are held to age-based expectations. And if we have dysmaturity, if we're not making it for whatever reason, people don't understand; they assume that our quirks/behaviors are intentional. So we're all blamed and shamed and sometimes even punished for things that we can't control. That naturally leads to a lot of anxiety.

Jessica: Absolutely.

Patti: Some of us can do something or know something one day, and that's gone on another day. We have on days and off days. And that can apply to memory. It can apply to abilities; it can apply to socialization. Sometimes we're confident, and other times we just want to turn into, you know, the wallpaper. That in itself creates so much anxiety.

Jessica: Absolutely. And it can lead to depression, having a short fuse, or withdrawal. You know, where we just disappear into ourselves.

Patti: Those behaviors aren't so much tied to our brain-based differences but rather to the poor fit between our abilities and the things that people expect of us.

Jessica: Absolutely. And I definitely think that played a huge part. I was considered a smart, engaged kid. And so it was very perplexing to the adults around me that there were some things that I just was not adapting to. I would also say that my presentation, as with many individuals with FASD, as being smart and articulate, is often why FASD is so hidden. It's why I feel so compelled to speak about my experience - because I was told again and again and again, "You're capable. You're like everybody else, just as smart, just as able as everybody else, and you should be achieving what everybody else is."

Patti: "You could do it if you tried harder."

Jessica: Yes! Another common suggestion that I took to heart and internalized was my own failings. It was a heavy burden. My mum raised my brother and me to believe in ourselves and our own strength and capacity. She wanted us to feel completely supported and capable of fulfilling our dreams and desires. Unfortunately, the level of support and type of support needed is so vastly different for a child with FASD than for a typical kid. It seemed that everyone felt that I should perform a certain way because my intellect seemed to indicate that I would, but I wasn't. This was significant because it really damaged my sense of self. I considered myself to be someone who could achieve a high standard, and the kids I hung around with were in the top tier; they were all high achievers. They graduated in the top 1% of the school. That was my social group. I was the only one not performing within that social group, and it was excruciatingly painful and destroyed my self-esteem.

Patti: I was kind of the opposite because I didn't have a social group. I was a loner because people lost friends by befriending me. So I just turned inward and did my own thing. Where I lived, our high school was developed by the state of Pennsylvania to be an example of what public education could and should be. We had three resource centers, plus the general library. We had a planetarium. We had five or six gyms and dance studios. We had three cafeterias. We had a bigger campus than any of the community colleges out here in California that I have seen. It was a huge campus. As girls back in the 70s, we were not brought up to marry doctors and lawyers. We were brought up to *be* doctors and lawyers.

Jessica: That's so cool.

Patti: My IQ was high, so I so I did not struggle. Our English department had thirty-one different classes. That's more than the University of Pittsburgh offered.

Jessica: That's crazy.

Patti: I chose not to take the AP (Advanced Placement) English class, where you had a few weeks of this and a few weeks of that, rotating through many different subtopics. I took an entire semester on satire. I took an entire semester on poetry. I took a college-level writing class. Taking English classes for my electives enabled me to graduate a year early. I could not stand my stepfather, so I ran away to college when I was sixteen.

Jessica: I did not perform well enough to get into university when I finished high school. I went to uni (university) later, at the age of twenty-five. Well, that's not entirely true. I was accepted into an arts degree. It was a considered placement as I hadn't made the cut-off, and it was at a school I really didn't want to go to. I'm so glad that I didn't go, because I had no clue. There's no way I would have managed. It would have been a disaster. I didn't know how universities even functioned... I thought it was like high school. I absolutely did not have the academic, executive, or adaptive function to undertake tertiary study at 17. When I did finally study at 25, undiagnosed and unsupported, it quite literally nearly killed me. But I did it.

Patti: Then add to that dysmaturity, and lacking the ability to assess risks – not nearly enough to stay safe in a college environment.

Jessica: Yeah, exactly. Prior to high school, I was at the top of my class academically. But in high school, they introduced self-directed learning, they introduced homework, they introduced a different style of teaching, and I plummeted to the bottom of all my classes because I couldn't do the work that way. It was never addressed by the school. No one said, "Oh, well, hang on, we've got this bright student, this smart student who is polite and well-behaved, who's not disruptive in class, performing really poorly, very suddenly." I hadn't changed schools or anything. I had the same teachers, ultimately. But my grades plummeted, and instead of asking, "Hey, what's going on here," it felt dismissive. "Oh, well, she's just a lazy teenager, and she's just going through a phase, so she's not doing the work." But that just wasn't the case at all. I was trying desperately to keep up. There were many, many times in my high school experience when I had nowhere to sit at lunch. So I was by myself. I used to go to the toilet stalls and cry, or I hid in the library because I had no one to sit with.

Patti: So, what were your young adult years like? How many of these struggles carried over into those transitional years? The transition from child to adult is difficult for everyone to navigate, but which one of your quirks made that transition particularly challenging for you?

Jessica: Oh, it would have to be my executive and adaptive functioning; I really struggled in knowing how to find the resources I needed, coordinating and prioritizing things I needed to do, *starting* those things, working out the quickest point from A to B… and it wasn't until much later that I've realized how much the auditory stuff affected me. I was not a happy camper. I definitely had very high anxiety and depression, but I was determined. I was really quite stubborn. I was very determined to "adult". I became increasingly fatigued. I had ongoing problems with iron deficiency anemia, which is, of course, a very common comorbidity of FASD. There was damage to my nervous system, but I didn't hadn't yet learned about that. I was just having these issues of unknown causes. So I believe I had been on a very slow but steady decline physically. I basically didn't really know how to launch my life. As a young adult, I worked many jobs. I didn't know that

126

life wouldn't progress if you didn't take *the right* action. But I didn't know what actions to take or how to take them. I watched my peers and really thought that I was doing as they did... to the best of my ability. By 2008, I had moved to Melbourne. But by the end of that year, I was so debilitated by anxiety that I literally couldn't walk down the street without having a panic attack.

Patti: Oh, that's a painful way to live.

Jessica: I was really debilitated, and I had health issues that can all be related back to the alcohol exposure. For example, with my central nervous system, things with my guts, my head, and my muscles. I had tachycardia but didn't realize I had tachycardia. I wasn't integrating into my new community at all. I was incredibly shy and had really high anxiety. I moved to Melbourne to go to university, but it took me four years to apply because I kept getting scared, didn't know how to approach it, and didn't know how to do it. By the end of 2008, early 2009, I recognized that I actually needed help. There was something wrong. So I went to a women's health clinic and was advised to see a psychologist, which I did. I did CBT (Cognitive Behavioral Therapy) for a couple of years, and my Psychologist absolutely kept me afloat long enough to complete my UNI Diploma. But by the end of school, I was much worse - in a really bad way. My health, both physically and emotionally, had been totally degraded. I was incredibly ill. I was bedridden. And very lonely. Over the next five years, I was pretty atrociously "gaslit" by the medical profession. I was so poorly taken care of that my mum intervened in my health care because she had begun to seriously feel that I would not live. It was a very rough time.

Patti: I can just imagine the relief you must have felt reading about that survey that the FASD Changemakers did.

Jessica: Right. Absolutely. It shocked me greatly. I watched one of the YouTube clips of Emily, CJ, and Myles talking about the results. I remember Emily talking about her tachycardia. I was blown away. I was absolutely blown away! But by then, I did have a good idea of what those symptoms pointed toward.

127

Patti: So what made you consider FASD as a possible unifying factor in all of what you struggled with?

Jessica: I didn't. What happened was I became so sick that with Chronic fatigue, POTS, depression, and everything else that, I could no longer function; my body completely shut down. I was bedridden after the smallest exertion. I would have to hold on to the soap dish or sit down to shower so I wouldn't pass out. My mum stepped in. I was about twenty-six years old and living about 2,000 kilometers from home. I had moved from northern New South Wales down to Melbourne, Victoria. I was on the phone with my mum a lot, crying and telling her I just didn't know what was wrong and why I couldn't do anything, and how horrible and how hard life was. Every few weeks, I went to the doctor's office. They kept telling me that I was fine. Chronic Fatigue Syndrome didn't even register. I had shared what I knew of my birth history, that it was a traumatic birth. I knew my birth story. So if at any time during my entire health battle, which has spanned more than a decade, a doctor or specialist or a clinician had asked about prenatal alcohol consumption, I would have been able to confirm that, yes. No one ever asked about that. So I spent five years being gaslit and doing cognitive behavioral therapy and being told that all my executive functioning problems and all my adaptive functioning problems, which were significant, were due to anxiety and depression. They told me that if I recovered from the anxiety and depression, I would be fine. But it's the other way around!

Patti: Exactly! The anxiety and depression are the *result* of never being understood, of never having one's voice truly heard, of never being able to make sense of yourself and the world. They are the *outcome* of a poor fit between our abilities and what is expected of us!

Jessica: So, one day, I was on a video call with my mum. I was incredibly distressed. My complexion was gray. I was incredibly sick. She recognized how sick I was.

Patti: She must have been terrified!

Jessica: She was. She basically thought if there was something physically very, very wrong, and that if whatever that was didn't kill me, she was afraid

I would kill myself because of how much of a mess I was emotionally. So my mum then started calling around to specialists to try and figure out what was wrong. She offered to take over my health care. She said, "I will take you to the specialist. Something is wrong. You're not getting what you need. We're going to fix this. We need to fix this." So I started seeing different types of specialists. I did a whole gamut of testing. That led to me being diagnosed with Chronic Fatigue Syndrome and POTS (Postural Orthostatic Tachycardia Syndrome). My capacity was pretty low. Energy-wise, I was booming and busting. I still have a lot of issues with my energy and my fatigue. But I'm a lot better... but it's been years and years of recovery.

Patti: I've never heard that phrase before. I kind of like it.

Jessica: My busting phases could last for months. I could be bedridden. I literally could not raise my hands above my head to change my shirts because the exertion was too great. So my mum was actively researching all of my symptoms and trying to get me to the right specialists and trying to work out what was happening. I got these two diagnoses of POTS and ME/CFS. These diagnoses made sense. They fit. But emotionally, I was shot, you know? I was absolutely at my lowest. It was really awful. I felt like there was no purpose for me to be on this planet. I felt I had no use or worth. We first looked at autoimmune disorders, but that didn't fit. The different therapies for CFS and POTS helped but didn't really explain a lot of things that were still happening. So mum was still searching. It was a bit of luck how she stumbled upon FASD. Maybe it was meant to be. She happened to be watching a television show, a news program. The episode was on FASD. The guest that they interviewed was a woman, who is a wonderful Australian advocate, and a parent to two grown kids with FASD. As mum was watching that, she said, "Oh my God. This is what is happening to my daughter."

Patti: I can imagine the depth of your mum's pain at that moment!

Jessica: It was a lot for her.

Patti: Absolutely. I just want to give her a big hug.

Jessica: Thank you. I'm sure she would really appreciate that. My mum, you know, she's so brave, and she's so fierce. You know, she's so, don't you make me cry.

Patti: It is a lot for her to come to grips with. When I asked my mom if she drank when she carried me, she answered, "Oh, yeah, every day." Back in the 1960s, nobody knew it would harm the baby. She wasn't at all curious why I asked her. I'm not even sure I want her to read this book because I don't want her to wrestle with guilt in her last months or years.

Jessica: My mum, you know, she's just... she's fierce. She's bold and beautiful. She loves us fiercely. She wants what's best for us. When she saw this episode, she was like, "Oh, my God, this is what we need to look at." So then she started calling around the national FASD organizations, doing her research, and seeing what fit. When she looked at the behaviors and the symptoms of FASD, she was like, "Oh, my God, oh, my God, this is her!" Everything was coming together. Then she approached me about it. She very gently suggested that I ask my psychiatrist to do a neuropsychological examination because she thought that I had FASD. She explained FASD to me and why she thought I had it. I rejected it outright. I was not strong enough emotionally (to take it in). I was too much of a mess. I couldn't possibly accept it because I didn't understand how the brain works. My first reaction was to ask her, "How can you say that? Mum, you're telling me I'm dumb. You think I'm stupid. You don't think that I'm going to achieve anything. How could you say that? How could you?" I had so much internalization during my school years around not performing, not feeling smart, and feeling worthless. I was like, "Oh my God, my mom is telling me I'm stupid."

So I really kicked back, and I was not nice about it. I did not accept what she was suggesting. Because we have so few FASD-informed medical professionals, my opinions were corroborated by the doctors I was seeing. They reacted with, "Oh, you don't present that way. I don't think that's a problem for you." So I spat that back at my mom. Sadly, that was a very difficult time for her and for our relationship. And it was a very difficult time for me as well. I was very sick. My mom was very worried. My denial put back the process for a year. I did not want her to try to speak to me about it every time we saw each other or spoke. I would simply not accept it. So over the course of that year, she compiled a history of my life and, from a medical standpoint, how FASD fit me as an individual.

Patti: I admire your mom.

Jessica: Oh, thank you. I admire her too. She's a strong, resilient, fierce woman who went above and beyond despite the stigma, despite the lack of available services, which is none for adults. There's none. So during that year, my mum compiled all the information, and she organized it into three big folders of clinical and personal information and how it links. When I went to visit her at the end of that year for the Christmas holidays, she said, "I will take you on a holiday to New Zealand. *If* you read these folders. If after you read these folders you still do not believe that you have FASD, I will not talk to you about FASD ever again." I was about half an hour into the material, and I burst into tears. I was like, "Oh my God, this is me!" It seemed like it was written about me. I just cried and cried and cried. It took me another three years to get the diagnosis because there are so few places where, as an adult, you can get a diagnosis. It took us a lot of research to find out how I could get the diagnosis. I did get a neuropsychological assessment. They could not diagnose FASD as it was not their expertise, but it became clear where my deficits were; during this time, mum had been communicating with the national FASD organizations, trying to get help in knowing which direction to go, to get the right information, the right assessments – whatever would be needed to make a full diagnosis. But we were having a lot of trouble. We went to a geneticist, which was a pretty awful experience. He laughed at me first off, then smirked and laughed and rolled his eyes during my appointments with him when I asked about assessment for FASD. He basically told me that I couldn't possibly have FASD. He straight up said, "There's no way that you have FASD because you don't have epileptic seizures."

Patti: What? That's ridiculous. I'm gobsmacked on that one! I have no words for that degree of ignorance!

Jessica: We had no one to confirm FASD. Mum had gone and looked for my birth records, and we added my birth records to my huge binder of medical history. Through the connections that we had made through the FASD organizations, we were given the chance to meet with a pediatric specialist for a case review.

131

Patti: That's the same thing that Rebecca did. She went to a pediatric specialist.

Jessica: Yeah, because there's no one assessing adults. There are some multidisciplinary clinics in Australia, but they are few and far between. There's none in Victoria, where I live. They were trying to build one, but I don't think it's gotten off the ground. They're very limited and will only see children between certain ages. I also hear there's a two-year waiting list. So there was no one to assess me except the pediatric specialist. He reviewed all the information we brought him, and he measured my facial features properly. He examined my baby photos and assessed my face. And I finally got the diagnosis just before I turned thirty-three.

Patti: That means is alcohol was consumed on days 17-21. There has always been a myth that gets under my skin. That FAS is the "most severe kind" because it includes the facial features.

Jessica: Yes, exactly. People want to put our level of functioning on some kind of linear path like we're either high (functioning) or low or somewhere in between. But it can't be assessed that way. We can't be kind of judged that way.

Patti: Right! You can have an IQ of 135 and still need support.

Jessica: Absolutely. In my advocacy, I really try to express that the way FASD presents is often hidden. I had a much-hidden nature in my presentation. But my symptoms are still legitimate. I still have significant deficits despite my language skills.

Patti: Yes, just because we have strong expressive language doesn't mean that we have strong receptive language skills.

Jessica: And it doesn't mean that I don't have significant problems with executive functioning, adaptive functioning, learning, memory, attention, and all of those things. All of those things hindered me greatly and resulted in my complete failure to launch (into independent adulthood). I am now nearly thirty-seven years old, and I have significant intervention services and support. I do yards of physio and therapy to recover from the trauma that I experienced from my experiences. I understand what happened to me is what so often happens when our FASD is not identified.

Patti: We are so misunderstood to our very core about what our capacities are. Everybody has so many expectations for us that we can't meet because of the way our brain is wired, which of course, is different for each one of us. I just lost my train of thought.

Jessica: Oh my god. I'm exactly the same. Even if I remember the words that I was supposed to say, I will forget what the point was.

Patti: Yep. Which is why so many of us interrupt people because we know we have a really good point to make, and we're going to forget if we wait.

Jessica: Yeah. I have to say it instantly. Otherwise, I've completely forgotten. I've learned,

Patti: I've learned to put those thoughts down on paper.

Jessica: Yeah. I'm still not amazing at that. Like, I have good runs, basically. I might have a really good run of like keeping on top of things, but if one thing falls apart, everything falls apart. Then I need someone to actually put me back in the routine and get me back there. I can't necessarily do it on my own.

Patti: So, let's just move forward a little bit more. So you have your diagnosis. Everything completely makes sense. You finally get the vindication of a diagnosis. What are you doing now to pave the way forward for our (FASD) community?

Jessica: Well, I guess for me, it was such a knock to realize that I had FASD. I've learned through that process how the brain actually works, though I'm no expert by any stretch of the imagination. I've learned what brain-based behavior looks like and what the difference is between a personality trait and brain-based behavior. Having that understanding and

133

how that looks in real life absolutely blew my mind. I instantly became passionate that everyone needed to know this. Everyone needs to understand that certain behaviors are not character traits or dysfunction but simply a function of the brain and how that brain responds to things. My first reaction was to think, "Wow, this is incredible information. How did I not know this? And why doesn't anyone else know this? Why don't the social workers, and the clinicians, and the doctors know this!?" Because I feel like this information, about how the brain works and what brain-based behavior looks like, is so integral to a myriad of diagnoses and understanding of what is going on for a person.

Patti: I totally understand that response. I'm with you on that!

Jessica: I was compelled to share the power of diagnosis and how that has completely changed my life and my sense of self. I know the stats... I know how many Australians are really struggling, and FASD is being widely ignored. I have to speak about it. There has been a complete rewriting of what success looks like for me. There has been a complete rebuilding of my sense of self, of my confidence. I would say that I'm not fully there yet, but I do have a lot of a lot more joy and support. After my diagnosis, a weight was lifted off me; I could breathe again. I could stop blaming myself. Some of the experiences that I had growing up were so alienating and ostracizing and lonely and painful and humiliating, and so *avoidable.* Minor accommodations could have completely changed my outcomes. I don't feel that any human deserves to feel how I felt in my life and to feel so worthless and so unable to achieve. Prior to diagnosis, I really felt that the world would be better off if I was dead. Sometimes, I would wake up and be like, "Please just let it be over. Please just let my life be over." I never harmed myself, but I would look up at the stars, and I would beg for my life just to be over because I couldn't deal with what was happening. Then I started reading statistics, and I realized there are literally hundreds of thousands of Australians, and millions of people worldwide, that present like me and are hidden in society, who are floundering and who are struggling and who are beating themselves up and who are killing themselves and who are in despair.

Patti: They are who this book is for.

Jessica: There were so many individuals who are being told that it's their fault, that it's their anxiety, that it's their depression, that it's because they are not smart enough or they're not trying hard enough, or they're not doing this, or they're not doing that. Their struggles are not about a lack of desire or want. It's not about a lack of enthusiasm or intention. It's not about a choice. No, it's about the limitations of those higher-order functions and adaptive functions that they are expected to have in order to navigate a society that does not consider or see them. Without these skills, living in this world is really bloody hard!

I couldn't continue the rest of my, hopefully long, life without sharing this experience and saying, "Hey, this needs to be recognized!" The gaslighting needs to stop! Women need to know what alcohol does to their children. I can't fathom not sharing what I have learned because of the pain in my soul... I went through all that trauma and pain and all that self-blame and all the false expectations — so much of that could have been avoided, and there could have been so much more joy, success, and a feeling of connectedness in my life.

Now at thirty-seven years old, I am only now healing. My entire life, Patti, has changed; my entire sense of self has changed. If I hadn't gotten diagnosed, I think I would have been dead by now. I want to have a life. I want to have a career. I want all the things that every other woman in their thirties wants. I want to drive a car. I want to go on adventures. I want a great husband. I want all those things too. I can't stay silent about what all I have learned because it was so shocking.

Patti: Yes. We cannot unlearn what we've learned!

Jessica: Exactly!

Patti: We are forever changed by it, and it's not about our wanting to blame our sucky lives on our mothers; that's not it at all! It has nothing to do with that! It's about reframing our experiences as being the result of an invisible, physical disability with behavioral symptoms. I hate the term disability, but the world is pathology-focused. We can do anything with support, but without that support, we are definitely handicapped.

Jessica: I do very much appreciate that there are many individuals who are really triggered by the word "disabled," and they don't want it applied to them, but for me, that word is a savior. I actually have a very different relationship with that word because that word shifts all the shame, all the sadness, all the grief, and all the self-loathing that I experienced and actually puts it somewhere else! Because I was diagnosed as an adult, everything before was deemed to be my fault. But with the label of disability, I've actually been able to convert that self-blame into something "other." So for me, it's a helpful word.

Patti: I kind of struggled with the concept of disability for a long time. The government considers Type 1 Diabetes to be a disability, but, even though I was diagnosed in 1965, I never considered it to be a disability until 2011 when I realized that my brain no longer responded to dangerously low blood sugars by kicking out physical symptoms that would clue "me" into what was going on in my body; *that's* when, for me, it became a disability. Then almost a year later, when I got my diabetic alert dog, I discovered the pushback and the stigma people face when their disabilities are invisible.

Jessica: It's so hard because I still have so many false and unreasonable expectations that get placed upon me because of how well I communicate. Unreasonable expectations that I place upon myself, too, let's face it. But my executive functioning is quite poor. I get overwhelmed very quickly, but I speak well, so people think I can do everything else well too.

Patti: I know. People still say, "Drink 'till it's pink." But it's too late by then!

Jessica: We don't talk enough about consuming low levels of alcohol enough and what even low levels of alcohol exposure do. You can't measure someone's lost potential!

Patti: So the survey you were part of – it shows that there is an increase of 206 times the risk factor for early onset dementia – let's talk about the lost potential there

Jessica: We have a very strong drinking culture here. There's a huge amount of stigma, and women will not talk about it. So I felt compelled that it was sort of my duty to put my hands up and say, "Hey, I have brain damage. This is what FASD looks like!" This gave me a sense of purpose. I spent my entire twenties sick and miserable, thinking that there was going to be nothing for me - nothing that I could do, that I could also do well, or that made me feel like I had a purpose in life. Initially, I was ashamed about my FASD, like, "Don't tell anyone I have brain damage." But now, it has given me purpose. It's still difficult. People don't always want to accommodate me. I had individuals say they would be "enabling me"....uh, excuse me?

Patti: I think everyone who is neurodivergent is very skilled at wearing masks.

Jessica: Yeah, absolutely. I became very good at it, and I still do it without much thought

Patti: In dementia circles, the term for masking is called "show timing." It's as if you're up on stage, giving a performance. It isolates the full-time caregivers, who see the limitations daily because outsiders or infrequent visitors and healthcare providers only see the performances.

Jessica: Yeah, totally. It's like as soon as the door is closed, as soon as I'm home alone, that's when it all comes out. I had a three-day meltdown after my birthday last year because I was sensory-overloaded. I did not recover for three days. I was a mess, but no one knew that had happened. People invite me to loud, noisy environments. I can't. No one knows that when I was twenty-two years old, I couldn't make it on my own. I had moved to the city, but I couldn't buy a bed or set up my room because I didn't know how. My mum had to come down and buy a bed and a bookshelf for me because I didn't know how to navigate choosing a bed, having it delivered, or setting it up. At twenty-two years old, I didn't know how to do that. I hid that. After a year of sleeping on an air mattress, destroying my back, and being freezing cold, I burst into tears. My mum had to come and help once she knew. Now, I am working in a national capacity as a disability advocate and as an FASD advocate.

Patti: I am very proud of you, Jessica!

Jessica: Thank you so much! I am an advisory group member for NOFASD. I've worked on a number of projects with them. I'm also an advisory member of the FASDHUB.

These are our national organizations. I am a guest speaker at the University of Western Australia, where they have a postgraduate course for the assessment and diagnosis of FASD. I've also campaigned alongside the Foundation for Alcohol Research and Education.

I have been part of an advisory group for the University of Queensland as well as the University of Sydney, with different clinicians and researchers there. I have really just put my hand up for everything! I've been very busy. It makes me feel worthwhile, like I've got something to contribute to society... something positive, to change outcomes for individuals. I put my tidbits into different projects. I want people to really know what alcohol does, so they can make informed choices. I have done a number of webinars and have been on a number of podcasts also...

Patti: I love doing podcasts; they are so much fun! They remind me of when I was when I had to fundraise for my service dog, and I would go I would go on talk radio shows.

Jessica: I did a TV segment on a popular news program, with another wonderful advocate, at the start of 2022. That was a trip!

Patti: So, now you've joined the International Adult Leadership Committee of the FASD Change-makers.

Jessica: That's correct. I feel very cool doing that, and I've definitely got some things in the works. Our disability services are really lacking in FASD-informed support and understanding, so I'll be writing a submission for their review. I will write another submission for a book about neurodiversity in Australia. I'm really doing my best to get the word out there in every way that I know how. I'm also really trying to involve myself in the decision-making and policy-making around alcohol safety, the harms alcohol causes, and FASD in clinical training.

Patti: I am also involved in professional development training. A few weeks ago, I was talking with someone in Canada who had collaborated with someone who had this ingenious idea of putting pregnancy tests in every bar. His idea was that a female patron would have to show the bartender a negative test in order to be served alcohol. It's a great idea, but it would be controversial, for sure.

Jessica: Definitely a controversial idea here in Australia. Unfortunately, I think a large majority of women (those who don't struggle with dependency issues, of course) tend to defend with the "my body, my choice" argument as soon as someone says to them, "Please don't drink, you're harming the baby, and this is how." But no one is trying to disenfranchise women; we're trying to give them information so their babies are as healthy as possible. Obviously, if you gave your toddler a bottle of wine, that's a criminal offense.

Patti: Yes!

Jessica: So why would you do it while they're in your belly? I do appreciate there are many factors as to why women drink and that support is needed for women with alcohol dependency to abstain. The percentage of unplanned pregnancies in Australia is almost 50%.

Patti: It's 45% here in the States.

Jessica: It's a huge number!–We need to empower women with the information so that they know what the consequences of their choices are.

Patti: Exactly! Women do not deserve anyone's judgment. None of us knew what we didn't know until we learned it! Jessica, I so very much appreciate you juggling your schedule so that we could meet despite our nineteen hour time difference. What a wonderful conversation!

Married with FASD
A Conversation with Bill and Debbie Michaud

In this conversation, I speak with Bill and Debbie Michaud, both of whom have come to recognize their own impacts of prenatal alcohol exposure after fostering those who have been diagnosed with FASDs. Debbie is a social worker, and Bill is a family services worker but had formerly worked in disability services. Both have been involved in bringing FASD training to professionals across northwestern Ontario (province) for decades and have spoken at international conferences as well as on podcasts.

Patti: I am so grateful you both could join me for this conversation today and that you both wanted to participate in this project.

Debbie: Well, we really enjoyed the work that we did with Jeff, too (Podcast of Jeff Noble, The FASD Success Show). So this is just an extension of that. So what made me first consider FASD? I had never heard about FASD in my life. My mother was a chronic alcoholic, and I always knew that I struggled, but I didn't know why. And then, as I got a little bit older, I would ask my stepdad if I had ADHD, so I started to learn more about that. And then, I remember, I was sitting in an auditorium taking a course on childhood disorders for my bachelor's degree in social work. In the lecture, they mentioned FASD very briefly. My brain went ding, ding, ding. I had to leave the auditorium, go to the washroom and look at my face. I was in my early twenties then, and I just continued on with life. I didn't think any more of it until we started fostering. One of the first children we had long-term came to us with an FASD diagnosis that she received when she was four. So we started to learn more and more about that. You know how they describe somebody who has had a serious trauma -- how they can't look at it all at once?

Patti: Yes.

Debbie: So they'll get a little bit and then another little bit. That's what began happening with me. I started to realize, "I think I am impacted. Wow, this is crazy!" I kind of grew out of my (facial) features a little bit (as I got older). About fifteen years ago, I went to St. Michael's Hospital in Toronto, a diagnostic center. I asked if they would consider (evaluating me for) a diagnosis. I brought my report cards, I brought my pictures, everything like that. But the person there said to me, "You have a job. You work in child welfare?" I said yes. "You get up, and you go to work every day?" I answered yes. Then she said, "You can't have FASD." And *that* is one of my pet peeves. The idea that if you have FASD, you're not smart, you're not reliable, all of that. So that's a real pet peeve. But I don't think it was until I started writing the book about my mother – one day, I was looking through all our old family photos - that I realized, "Oh my goodness, I have *all* the features. Can you even believe that?" So I opened it up and showed my husband. So that was like the very last nail. I had seen that picture a thousand times, but I had never really seen it looking for the (FAS) features, and it took my breath away. I was just so shocked. There were pieces of me that were in denial along the way, too, because I didn't want to have a disability.

Patti: What about you, Bill?

Bill: She told me I did. (Laughing) Because we've both come from backgrounds with heavy drinking in our families and stuff like that. So for me, when we first fostered that little girl, Deb started getting into learning about FASD. I was always on the perimeter, just hovering around the outside, being supportive. She would teach me what she was learning, and I understood this and that. But never once did I ever think of myself or my partner (as having it). Deb started teaching family (and others in our family's life) about FASD. My mom says, "Oh, I wonder if that's what was wrong with Bill." Then my mom told us the story about how the doctors had advised her that because her husband drank lots, and she was stressed, that she should go out too and not have hard liquor but maybe draft (beer) or something. So she and my aunt would go out on Friday and Saturday nights and throw back a couple of jugs of draft. And yeah, I knew I was a hard kid to manage. Like, I (was a runner). They used a clothesline and tethered my harness to it before they would open the door. Because then I would bolt out of the door, just like (you see) in the cartoons. I was always getting into things, and taking things apart, all kinds of stuff. I never equated it (my behavior) to anything other than me being "bad," (When my mom said that), that's when (my behavior) came into focus for me a little bit more, and I began to consider, "maybe." It was a little harder for me, I think, to wrap my mind around. I'd rather go with ADHD, you know? That's my major piece from all of this (the ADHD symptoms): I roam around doing several things at once, and all of that type of stuff. So I do believe today that I do live with an FASD.

Patti: Well, you could live with both.

Bill: Well, that's part of it. There are so many different things that could (be part of FASD), and every day we hear about new things that are attached to FASD. So yeah, I think it's a direct result of that. And it's funny too because I've been like that my whole life. I think to myself, "Well, I'm an adult now, so that's (ADHD symptoms) supposed to stop," but it just changes. So I wander around the yard, and all the kids and my wife just go from window to window, watching me wander around the yard doing different things. So sometimes it (ADHD/FASD) can be tough. Other times it's great because it gives you focus like you've never had, to the point where it's almost detrimental. But again, you can focus. It's just a strange type of thing. It's like, phew.

Patti: Kind of like my focus on this book project lately. But I totally relate to the process you both went through because I first started with my interest in FASD six years ago when I transitioned to a post-adoption support program at the agency where I was working at the time. I had a friend whose kids were on the spectrum, so I had her come in to do a presentation for my agency's adoptive parents about FASD. She brought a friend with her, and the two of them did a marvelous job. I thought it was fascinating. I loved everything I heard. But it never dawned on me that what I was learning from them might apply to me. Then five years ago, I started studying with FASCETS, to become certified as a Facilitator of their neurobehavioral model. I recognized myself all over the place when they introduced a tool to us. I thought that was odd, but I still wasn't really connecting those dots. In one of the first sessions, they have a group exercise that normalizes neurodiversity, and the homework is to have family members do the exercise also. So I did it with my mother because she's a convenient guinea pig (I am her caregiver). If my husband had not sarcastically said, as he passed through the room, "Oh, so that's what's wrong with you," I may never have turned to her and said, "Mom, did you drink while you carried me?" She answered, "Oh, yeah, every day!" All of a sudden - boom - there it was! And you're right, Debbie, revelations do come in drips and drabs because it is too much to take in all at once!

Debbie: Right!

Patti: As you get one revelation, you have to process it and integrate it into how you see yourself before you're ready for the next truth to drop.

Debbie: Exactly. But the revelations are good though, too. Bill and I have serious sensory issues. For instance, I don't like somebody flicking my hair. That stuff is just enough to drive me crazy. (But he's always seen that as an affectionate act.) So we know now what that's about. It's not that he's not a good partner or that I don't love him. It's that I have this thing (sensory issue). And he's got memory issues. His memory issues are really, really bad. We've been married for twenty-six years now. He very rarely remembers an anniversary or a birthday or anything special like that, but because I know now that it's his memory issues, I just buy my own gift, and we call it a day.

Patti: And, bonus, that way, it's always what you want.

Bill: Yeah, or she tells me what she wants, and then I'll go grab it. Understanding that it's tied to FASD has been a big relief.

Debbie: Well, initially, you know, his memory was a big issue. He and I have fertility issues, which is why we adopted through foster care. The first Mother's Day that he missed? I almost divorced him. I was really, really upset, and it was because he didn't remember. It wasn't because he didn't love me. So the revelations have been really important for our relationship.

143

Patti: One of the reasons I was so excited to talk with you both together is to combat another myth that FASD means not having a family. My gosh, if one in twenty people are affected, of course, there are going to be tons of couples out there who are both impacted by prenatal alcohol exposure and whose challenges as a couple, when put in the proper understanding, don't need to lead to divorce court.

Debbie: That's right. It was developing an understanding of FASD that actually prevented that from happening to us!

Bill: So we have these mainstream expectations of what your partner would do for you.

Patti: Yeah?

Bill: We're learning all the time to adjust those expectations. I mean, even the whole cutting people off before they're finished talking like I tend to do. I figured out it's because I'm scared I'm going to forget what I was thinking about, so I interrupt people. So now, a lot of times, I'll write it down or look at my shoelace or something until I can talk. Things like that are still there. Those don't go away. And that's the other thing that's inconvenient too, is that you do some work on something, and you're like right on, but if you don't keep up with it, then (your progress) goes away. I wish it would be the other way - where you figure something out, and it goes into your stored memory, but that's just not the case, and that's *really* frustrating. It's very frustrating to have to go back to the store several times in order to get everything that you're supposed to get. As a male, that weighs on me. I expect more of myself. So I start to get a little depressed about it sometimes. I'm starting to realize that I have flare-ups, where I'll go for a while, and everything will be really good, and I'm doing things I'm supposed to do at work and blah, blah, blah. Then, all of a sudden, out of the blue, I realize that I haven't done this or that. Or it looks like I'm being lazy around the house. And it's like, "Oh, crap, it's happening again." So then you've got to rejig things. I've got to climb up the mountain again. You know, self-actualize for the 90th time this month. So that can be pretty tough.

Patti: So, is there anything that you do to give yourself grace around that?

144

Bill: Before, (I would just think) I'm screwed up. But now I know where it's coming from. But I also know that because I know some things, I should probably take care of things (complete tasks) better, but it's just that motivational piece, too. It's like you're just plodding along through life, and you really don't have a worry, but everything's kind of falling apart around you. But you don't even realize it because you don't have a worry. It's a nice place to be until the end when people are noticing. Then it's like, oh crap. That's the hard part. Then you got to stay on top of yourself because you know other people are watching. Unfortunately, my motivator is fear. It's almost like I have to get to that place before I can go forward, and that's frustrating.

Patti: Well, here's another topic: sharing with other people that we're living with FASD and from time to time struggling with aspects of it. I've only known for five years, and initially, sharing it was a bit like "coming out" as far as anxiety about the stigma. How long have you guys known?

Debbie: Because it's come in bits and pieces, there's not a really concrete time (that I came to awareness of FASD. My discovery process began in) 1992. I'm a very concrete person, which a formal diagnosis would provide (that concrete marker). I've been building up my awareness (since 1992). But I really, *really* knew when I looked at that picture of me with my mom. I'm still on the fence, to be honest. I do believe, I do, but there's always that but.

Bill: So, for me, I just feel fortunate that I'm not affected in some of the ways that I see other people affected. I really have to watch and try not have a "better than" attitude because I'm really no different – we (my clients and I) were running in the same circle. It's just the effects are different. So you had asked about pet peeves that people have about FASD.

Patti: Yes.

Bill: My pet peeve is that people will recognize that someone has the diagnosis of FASD and then go on to complain that the person "won't do this and won't do that; they're not doing this, and they're not doing that." At the schools, they just don't listen. (It's not enough to acknowledge that a student has) an FASD, without listening to the people who really A) know the individuals on a deeply personal level, like family, and B) sometimes other professionals don't work well with each other. So, you have someone who knows a lot about FASD and is helping a family, but the teachers and the doctors don't seem to want to be a part of the team.

Patti: That is very frustrating. I think, in part, that's a systems issue for a lot of reasons. At least where I'm from, systems don't like to get into the weeds with everything that FASD entails because then it's going to cost money. But none of us knew what we didn't know until we learned it. So, I think, on some level, people are well-intended, they're just ignorant.

Debbie: I agree with that, but it's more than just about the money. People don't want to do the paradigm shift (from a behavioral/compliance model to a neurodiverse model) because they don't want to question what they've always done, the way they've always done it, and the reasons that they've done it. They want to stick to that punitive model where people have to comply. They have a "This is the way that the system works, and this is the way it's always going to work" attitude.

Patti: Perhaps for neurotypical people.

Debbie: Not even though. That's the problem.

Patti: Because all our systems believe behavior is always intentional, all our systems are ineffective. Neurodivergence is a lot more than FASD. In fact, FASD is left out of most lists of neurodivergence.

Bill: Well, that's my other pet peeve. The fact of the matter is that FASD is the most prevalent cause of developmental disability, yet autism gets all the attention. Before autism, Downs Syndrome got all the focus. I've worked in developmental services for twenty-six years. There seems to always be only one focus (one favored diagnosis when it comes to funding.) When families of children with Downs quit being so demanding, the focus shifted to Autism. But they're staying so far away from FASD because everything has to change if you start addressing that. Autism and FASD aren't far apart in the ways people are impacted. So there wouldn't be that much change in what is provided, but they just don't want to go there.

Patti: Yes, it's frustrating. Do you think a piece of that is because FASD is so prevalent that the idea of one in twenty people is just overwhelming?

Debbie: I think that's a piece of it, but I also think another piece of it is that people don't want to admit that FASD exists because drinking is still a part of everything in our culture. Families don't want to admit that they used alcohol during pregnancy. And there's one more thing I was going to say that I can't remember. It'll come back. With FASD, there's a terrible culprit that caused that dissonance. But for these poor parents who have children with Autism, nobody knows what causes it. They're just having to deal with this thing that came out of the clear blue sky. But with FASD, we know somebody's harming that baby. So the parents need to just stop drinking.

Patti: But maternal abstinence doesn't help the babies, though.

Debbie: Exactly. Not at all.

Patti: But there was a shift with Autism too, though, because twenty to thirty years ago, it was blamed on "Refrigerator Moms." Those emotionally unavailable women who were so busy climbing the corporate ladder that they weren't attaching well or bonding well with their babies, so Autism was their fault. But finally, the world recognized the error of this theory. And I do have faith they will get to that (shift in understanding) with FASD as well, at some point. I think we're all eager for that to happen, and frustrated that it's taking so long.

Debbie: Yeah, exactly. We just received a report from the Ombudsman from Ontario about a young girl who was from this northern area and was sent to a big city. She has FASD, and she was very vulnerable. She fell into human trafficking immediately when she got there. Yeah. And so, you know, not only does FASD impact people (in the way they develop), but then their life experiences, because of it, impact them over and over again. Let us just to go back a little bit. Bill and I -- we were not very well-behaved children. We had lots of issues as kids. I think that it would be important to note that because parents should have hope! We had parents who really, really were committed to us, and that's the reason we "made it."

Bill: That's true because I had addiction issues to alcohol and drugs. I didn't go to school. I got one credit in high school. I stole. I was bad. What I thought and everybody else thought was that I was a bad kid. I talked in class. I was the class clown. All those things. Everybody had a label for me. "You're bad, you're this, and you're that." I was the black sheep or whatever. But, where was I going with that?

Debbie: We were just talking about our childhoods and how our committed parents actually made the difference.

Bill: That's right, yeah. I'm no different than any of these other young people, like I know that now. I was no different. The only difference I had was that 1) I didn't go into the (foster care) system, and 2) I had two parents. They were divorced, but they both still cared for me and put up with a lot of crap, I'll tell you.

Debbie: He stole from his mom on a regular basis.

Bill: Yeah, I did lots of very not good things. I have an addictive personality. If it's not substances, then it's golf, computers, or gaming. I started smoking a couple of times again since I quit, you know. Thankfully, no alcohol or drugs, but it's always something.

Patti: But that can also be attributed to the FASD. Messing with the dopamine centers, the Locus Coeruleus. That's the section that processes dopamine that leads to addictions, whether it's to substances or behaviors.

Debbie: Yeah, absolutely. When I was a kid, I talked early and I sang early. I used to sing songs to everybody, and I was that indiscriminate kid. I would crawl into anybody's arms. I would talk to anybody. I would sing to anybody. My mom said I would go around in the community asking her, "Hey, is that my dad?" because she was a single parent. I was really, really bad at school. I didn't read a book until I was nineteen. I got into a lot of trouble too. I left home when I was fifteen. I got pregnant when I was sixteen. I fell into addictions pretty hard when I was eighteen. I hitchhiked to Toronto - my parents wanted to kill me. I just made bad decision after bad decision after bad decision until I was twenty-five.

Bill: That's incredible because I went to treatment at twenty-five years old. That whole maturity thing, when was I going to start to mature? I know I was a very frustrating person, and I think I still am at times. But I frustrated people back then. And even in my jobs as an adult. My bosses would say to me, "You know, you're so good with this, but this, this, and that..." Stuff like keeping appointments. So part of me wants to think that I'm different from these young people who now I'm working with and who miss their appointments with me to do their assessments... but I'm not different. That was one of my learning things too, (as I wrapped my head around having FASD). In my past job, a behavioral therapist there would create accommodations for me. We had schedules that everybody could see. He started color-coding everything for me, like asking, "How about I put purple as something that needs to be booked?" The next thing you know, all my bookings are *done*. But before that? It was just a crap show. I kept losing bookings, and people were upset with me. What the behavior therapists recognized and put into place for me was like a miracle to me.

Patti: It's amazing what accommodations can do. When structures are put into place to help us with our shortcomings. My immediate supervisor and I had worked closely together for years and years. When I finally went to her and disclosed my FASD, her response was, "I'm not surprised." I'm like, "What?" Was I wearing my FASD out loud? She went on to explain that I would say or do odd things, and she would just say, well, that's just Patti. I was surprised that anyone other than my husband was irritated by my quirks. She directed me to disclose my FASD to the other supervisor, who was over her as well, and when I did, that supervisor said, "Well, now that you know, what are you going to do about it?" And I'm thinking, what part of accommodations did she not understand" Accommodations are environmental, for others to do.

149

Bill: I had a similar thing. I shared with a couple of people on our team, but I didn't feel that I could share that with the supervisor because he was dismissive of people with disabilities, which is not fortunate because (that's not a good quality for someone) in that role. (But like I was saying earlier), the supervisors acknowledged the diagnoses but not the effects of the disabilities and would complain that there "should have a three strikes rule." And I'm thinking, (if I say something about my FASD) because (they want a policy of) three strikes, I'll be out.

Patti: In the world of social services, I wish that I had the opportunity to educate all the county social workers because a lot of social workers bad-mouth the birth parents, complaining that the parents' plans aren't even that hard, so why can't they get it? Blah blah blah blah blah. It's so frustrating to me that if you realize that their children have the physical effects of drug and alcohol exposure and that substance use is so often a generational behavior, why would it be surprising that perhaps those birth parents have those same physical effects from what their parents did? These birth parents, if they're affected by FASD or drug exposure or trauma, just like their kids are, can do everything if you present it in the right way and make it possible for them by adjusting your expectations and putting appropriate accommodations or supports in place. I'm left wondering if maybe that's a piece of why the systems of care are not eager to embrace FASD. You know, there are just so many of us out there.

Bill: I think, too, that it takes a lot of work. I think with some of the other disabilities, the onus is on the individual, or the disability is obvious. But when it's an FASD, a lot of times, it's not so obvious. Deb says I have FAS features because I have really skinny lips.

Debbie: Oh, and a mustache too. When you shave that off, it's like...

Bill: Yeah, but I still don't see it, like, personally. I really don't, eh? She does, and that's fine, but most people don't. As we watched our kids growing up, the ones that didn't have facial features were treated so poorly compared to the children who had (FAS facial) features because it wasn't recognizable. (We would advocate for them, but it would be dismissed as) looking for sympathy, blah blah blah.

Patti: The three of us, we all have successful careers in the helping professions, so I think it's confusing to people that, on some level, we can be functioning so highly, doing so well, and in other ways, we need structures and support from outside of ourselves.

Bill: Yeah, it's a spectrum, just like autism. It's a spectrum. So, I mean, there are people that you wouldn't even know, but they have a diagnosis of autism. And then there are others on the other side of the spectrum where you absolutely know as soon as you see them. There are so many people floating around because no one's the same – there's no (stereotypical presentation). You can't cookie-cutter FASD because there are so many different things involved with FASD. 400 and some different disorders.

Patti: I think that's what you were getting to before, when you referred to other, more visible disabilities. Things that have more standardized supports to prescribe. If you have vision loss, you give them a cane. You give them a seeing-eye dog. If there's hearing loss, you give them hearing aids or cochlear implants, or you hook up their doorbell to flashing lights. You know, whatever the case is, there's just a few standard things that everybody gets, and that doesn't work with FASD.

Bill: When someone has the facial features and is profoundly impacted, they get services. But then you have people with a "scattered profile." That's the tricky one, because high intelligence, able to function, do this, do that, but can't make a meeting, spends their rent money, all of those types of things, and they're the ones who get treated so poorly because "You should know better. You can make your time stable; you have a job, you should know better!" But that's also part of how FASD presents.

Debbie: I know, it's very frustrating. For us, too -- we're terrible with money. Terrible. We could have retired ten years ago. But no, because we're terrible with money. But we enjoy ourselves, and we took our kids to really exciting places, and we've run up debt. We've been to Disney and Universal in Florida a few times. One of the tricks I have learned is to do things in bits and pieces. I can't sit and write for hours on end. I just can't just do that. So I get my best writing done on laundry days. But I can get a lot done if I write a bit, then get up and mull it over a little bit while I'm doing something

151

physical, and then get back to writing for another little chunk. I have lots of physical movement needs, and (meeting those physical needs helps me to focus on whatever my mental tasks are). So this weekend, I got lots of writing done because I was cleaning the whole basement while I was doing it. That's the only way I can sustain my attention - by having movement breaks.

Bill: I never got affected that way. I can stay motionless for hours, which bothers Deb. I will shut down, literally, and sit in one spot for hours.

Patti: My husband and I are very different that way too. He rides a minimum of 300 miles on his mountain bike up in the foothills every month so that he'll be able to be around to care for me if I need it due to all my health stuff.

Bill: You just reminded me of another thing that I struggle with. I'll do something, but then it's done. I used to cycle until I went on a long trip, and then I never touched the bike again. Same with computers; I built computers, and then boom, one day, literally, I just didn't do that anymore. That bothers me because there are a million things I want to do, and I think I want to do them for a long time, but once I figure it out, it just drops off my mind completely.

Patti: Maybe part of the fascination for you in those hobbies is in the figuring out of the thing.

Bill: My mom would tell stories all the time about when I was a kid in school. I would be doing math, I'd figure it out, and then I just refused to do it again. She would ask me why I wasn't doing my work, and I'd answer it was because I knew how to do it, so there's no point in doing it again.

Patti: I'll bet teachers were pretty frustrated with you.

Bill: Yeah. In grade five, I got thrown right over a desk by a teacher. He told my father he did it. I don't have any animosity towards that man. I can't imagine how hard it must have been to be in an authority role when I was

152

around. I frustrated everybody. I mean, you should never throw a kid over a desk or anything, but I remember that day, and I deserved it.

Patti: I don't think anyone deserves that.

Bill: But it was a different time and space back then. We know better today.

Patti: So, are you guys doing anything to contribute to the FASD community in some way, like advocacy or in your local community? Are you doing anything to raise awareness for FASD?

Debbie: For the last fifteen or twenty years, I've been working really hard in the area of FASD. I've been doing a lot of research, for example, I did my master's thesis on FASD. I've done lots and lots of training on FASD. I've been to Vancouver and Toronto to do training. I run the training unit at my agency, and lately, I've started focusing on other areas besides FASD, though I do plan to get back to FASD. I've found that there is a need to understand the impact of trauma and FASD together, and so that's probably where I'll go. A bunch of ladies and I did make a video called *Picture This, Life as a Parent of Children with FASD*. It was a photo-voice project and is up on YouTube. Okay. We were asked to come and open an international conference with that video.

Patti: When we first began talking about this project, you sent me the link. I liked it!

Debbie: That's right. So I've done lots of work through the years, though as of late, not so much. I kind of, lots of people have the ball now. I'm meeting many people, like you, who are doing a good job picking up where I left off.

Patti: I'm wondering if maybe that's one of the differences between the advocacy for FASD and the advocacy for Autism. The advocacy within the autism spectrum community is *so* strong, but their voice is collective, whereas, with FASD, we don't really have that collective presence.

Debbie: I think we do (have a collective voice) in Canada. We have a ton of international conferences. COVID changed that somewhat; that's when I stopped actually doing my work on FASD publically. My very last public engagement was an FASD conference that I was speaking at right before COVID hit. And so a lot of that work just sort of dwindled after that. Bill and I were scheduled to do a conference in Red Lake, him and I, but we couldn't do that. I think in Canada, there is a collective voice, but I think maybe the understanding of trauma is sort of taking over and overshadowing FASD because it looks the same. And how many young people do we have who have FASD plus trauma, and we're just focusing on the trauma.

Patti: Yes, and how much of a child's trauma is caused by people not understanding their FASD?

Debbie: Exactly. That's what I realize when I look at my mother's story, and the physical abuse she and her disabled brother endured is unimaginable. My mother talks about both of them going for X-rays, and they had scars all over their heads. She talks about her father, one of her brothers, and banging his head against the crib bars because he wouldn't stop crying. So I agree with you completely; a lot of times, the trauma is caused by the misunderstanding and the frustration in the behaviors of the child with FASD.

Patti: Or the trauma is caused by school districts who don't understand FASD.

Debbie: We're talking about brain injuries. You cannot reward or punish away the effects of brain injury. You can't. It can't be done. Rewards and punishment will work with some kids with FASD inconsistently but won't work with others. We have actual FASD classrooms in some of our communities.

Patti: I've heard that. I'm so jealous.

Debbie: Well, my children were in one of those (specialized classrooms), and we helped to develop it. And by the time my one son was in grade five, they decided he was good enough to leave the classroom. So they transitioned him out of a classroom that was working for him at a very sensitive time in his life. That next year he was suspended - how many times after he was transitioned out? Bill had run out of holidays (vacation days). So we decided that we'd homeschool him, and he didn't go to (public) school for three years. There's this idea that somehow somebody can transition out of their support. You can outgrow the need for support.

Patti: Yeah. Outgrow your brain injury.

Debbie: I think what they're trying to do or trying to say is that the kids get to a point where they don't need the support. We know our kids get to a point where they need *different* supports, but what schools try to do is say, "Oh, no. They're at a point now where they don't need any support in the classroom." We tried to say that as kids mature, the support structure has to change with them. But that brings on a lot of different things - new challenges. I used to explain to the kids because they get frustrated, the rules change. So I kind of figured it out in my head. For instance, so this is grade four, they're going into. So in the summertime, we talk about there's a new set of social rules at school. You're going to be expected to do this and do that and do this. And it helped a little, but not enough to mainstream them. No matter what we said or did, the school agreed and did what they wanted anyway. The schools still do not acknowledge that most of the children who were mainstreamed ended up dropping out because they were unable to manage the mainstream transition.

Patti: I know so many parents here who go through that same experience, though not from FASD-informed programming.

Debbie: Because almost all the kids that were in that classroom now are no longer in school. One thing we've learned, though, through parenting several kids with FASD, when our children's path has been other than what we had hoped for, is that once they turn twenty-five to thirty years of age, they come into their own. They clean up their lives. I don't worry anymore. And *that's* (saying something because) I'm a highly anxious person. That's part of my disability. I don't think I have enough neurotransmitters running through my body to calm me down, but my kids are one thing I don't worry that much about anymore. I know they're all going to be okay.

Patti: So with the (parenting) experience comes the faith that there will be a leveling out. With immaturity, it's not that they don't mature. It's that the timeline is longer.

Debbie: Yeah. Right.

Patti: But even neurotypical kids don't grow up till they're twenty-five. I think for most people, adult reasoning settles in around twenty-five, though for those of us on the spectrum, it might be thirty-five, but we do get there.

Debbie: Exactly.

Patti: It seems like those transitional years are so much more of a challenge than they are for the typical child.

Debbie: Yes, they are.

Patti: I think that's when I worried my parents the most was during those years. You know, I started college when I was sixteen. Academically, I was ready. But socially? I lacked practice. The five years prior to running away to college dorms were spent in our sewing room, avoiding my stepfather. I was the best-dressed kid on campus. I dressed better than my professors did. But I was not equipped to manage the social temptations that exist on a college campus. So I made a lot of foolish decisions. I didn't recognize social risks, which is a very common problem.

Debbie: It's too bad that we live in a world where you have to be able to recognize risks, though. Wouldn't it be nice if we lived in a world where there were none of those risks?

Patti: Especially for girls. Just like you mentioned that your ombudsman said, immediately upon getting to the large city that the girl was sent to, she fell victim to trafficking.

Debbie: Yeah, for sure.

Patti: So, when I look back on those years – they were so shame-filled for me for so long. I ask myself, "How could I have been so stupid?" Grace came with understanding that not seeing the risks was a direct effect of the FASD.

Bill: You know, it's interesting. I was just thinking as you were talking about school. I used to say that addicts could find other addicts anywhere in the world. But I'm starting to believe that it's not addicts. I'm starting to believe that people who have FASD will find another person who has FASD no matter what, no matter where. You can be in the Antarctic, and you're going to find a penguin with FASD. I always thought it was the addiction piece, but it's not. It's like-minded people. I got along with them and got into trouble with them too. Because you gel. You understand each other.

Patti: I think that's true for being neurodivergent, period.

Bill: Yeah, exactly.

Patti: Living outside the box.

Bill: When we met, it was less than three months before we knew we were going to get married. We were married within a year of meeting. We only waited because we knew other people would think we were crazy. And it's been twenty-six years now, so it's been crazy.

Patti: Yeah. So my husband and I met online. It was a website for singles of our particular denomination. He wrote to me on Labor Day, and we were married six weeks later.

Debbie: Oh, well, there you go. See?

Patti: Mostly because it was six weeks of serious communication, not going somewhere to be mutually entertained. At the time, I figured we had probably a year and a half of conventional dating sandwiched into those six weeks. Long-distance relationships are hard, too. So being cross-country, because I was in Tennessee and he here in California, you can't do that forever. Would I recommend that? No. No way. But we've been married for almost twenty-four years.

Debbie: Online wasn't very popular back then. You were really brave.

Patti: Well, it was right when the movie You've Got Mail came out. And I had learned something from my previous mistakes; I knew he was a church elder, so I went to the church's website and emailed all the other elders and deacons for reference checks. I wasn't going to come to meet him if his story didn't check out.

Bill: You were talking over AOL.

Debbie: That's crazy!

Patti: Yeah. The plan was that I would come out here for a week to job and house hunt, and then he would visit me in Chattanooga. We were then going to decide where we were going to live. I got here on a Friday. We got married on Monday. And Thursday, when I talked to my mom (she knew I was coming), she said, "Well, don't do anything stupid." To which I said, "Too late, Mom, I already married him." You could have heard a pin drop. But it has worked for us! No, I wouldn't recommend anyone moving that quickly into a committed relationship, absolutely not, but it has worked for us. Had it been ten years earlier, it probably would not have worked.

Debbie: So something interesting, too. I was just thinking about your mom, and I wanted to tell you about my own mom. So my mom told me when I was young that she got pregnant with me while drinking a bottle of wine. She drank regularly throughout the pregnancy, except for when she was sick because she got terrible morning sickness. But when we learned about FASD, taught her about FASD, and talked to her about her own probable FASD, she said, "I never drank during my pregnancy with you, never." So there's a lot of shame there.

Patti: Yes. I think, too, about all the families that I've dealt with in more than two decades working in child welfare: women are forced to confess to using illegal substances during pregnancy because their babies test positive for it. So they're forced to do that. But what about alcohol? Women who already feel shamed are not going to also admit to using alcohol, which is legal. Why would you admit to it and take voluntarily take on that shame for something that's legal? But it's also a little bit of how the question is asked in the hospital.

Debbie: Absolutely.

Patti: If the doctor or nurse says, "You didn't drink while you were pregnant?" tells you how you're supposed to answer.

Debbie: Yes.

Patti: But if the doctor or nurse instead asks how far along a woman was when she found out she was pregnant, and what was going on during those couple months beforehand? What was life like? – It's far less threatening. We have to do better! At the time of delivery is a great opportunity for early identification and support!

Debbie: I've been learning about FASD, like I said, since 1992. I think in Canada, we've made a lot of strides, especially in this little community. In this little community, we have talked about FASD for a long time. And we have partnered with other agencies and brought in really important guest speakers. Jeff Noble and Reinier DeSmit were here right before COVID. RJ Formanek was here. Dan Dubofsky has been here. Diane Malbin was here. Donna DeBolt was here. So we've had lots and lots and lots of training, lots of teaching, lots of really great things in a community of 5,000 people.

Patti: Wow, that's amazing. How... Were you working with other communities also?

Debbie: Our small community is a hub for the North. So it's a really busy community. My agency and Bill's organization both an office here as well as offices in one of the bigger cities. So we would have these big conferences, and people would come from everywhere. Northwestern Ontario (province) is kind of like one big community.

Bill: Yeah. But it's so spread out. Like, we're an hour from the main highway. We have a secondary highway coming up to us, but to get to the main highway, we're an hour away from it. Yeah.

Debbie: So our community has done some really, really great things. And we've been a part of it, Bill and me, over the years.

Patti: What an honor!

Debbie: Yeah. Yeah. Yeah.

Patti: Quite a legacy that you both have been part of.

Debbie: Yeah, it's been great. Yep.

Patti: Any other pet peeves that you guys have?

Debbie: Oh, I had a few. (We talked about) my pet peeve is that people who have FASD are not smart. Another one is that they can't be parents.

Patti: Yes! You know, bringing people's children into a place of safety or into care because they (the mothers) have FASD, and they can't be parents. But you know, they *can* be parents with the right support. I think it all depends on the nature of what are their challenges? You can do all kinds of things if you have the right support.

Debbie: Exactly, yeah. What else? (pauses) Of course, they're bad, and they're lazy. That people with FASD are bad and lazy. That's a *real* pet peeve. That they need a diagnosis. You know, a diagnosis is like a golden ticket. "Okay, we will accommodate this child, we will do all of these things, but they *need* that piece of paper."

Patti: Yeah. I run into that down here too.

Debbie: So, the refusal to do the paradigm shift (from a behavior/compliance paradigm to a brain-based differences paradigm) without the diagnosis.

Patti: That really is a bothersome one because there are so few diagnostic centers, even for children. But so many adults are going to be like us, self-identifying. Where do they go? The reality is that if you recognize it, you get verification if you can, if your parents are still living, but you live *as if* (the diagnosis is in place.)

Debbie: That's right! But a lot of people refuse to do that, or they'll *try,* and they'll get just to a certain place (in their journey), and then that child or that person will piss them off, and then they're done. They stop living "as if" anymore. They go right back to that automatic, punitive perspective.

Patti: Yeah, and that's a shame. We have to do better with that too. I was looking at the stats, just using American numbers. So, based on the estimated 2022 census, if you look at 5% of the adult population, that's 16.6 plus million people. And if you think 10% get diagnoses, 90% don't. So, that's still a sickening number of people who have no idea that there's a biological basis for the struggles that they've had in life. I've seen stats that put the diagnostic rate at only 1%, which is abysmal.

Debbie: Mm-hmm.

Patti: They don't deserve that.

Debbie: Exactly! Another thing that really upsets me, too, are the systems we have. Social service systems are so complex that you need a Ph.D. to navigate them. And then (to have) the expectation that these people (with disabilities) are going to be able to navigate a system that's designed for them. Like Ontario Disability, for example, it is such a complicated system you need an advocate to access it. What is the point? So that stuff really bugs me too.

Bill: They do that for a lot of people (with various disabilities) - it's almost like they make systems so hard to even access (on purpose. Even just) the phone system (Phone trees are so hard to navigate. And then it is. It's infuriating.

Patti: Yeah. The whole disability structure is to get disability payments. You know, right away, that there's going to be 100% denial. There's no approval until someone makes a fourth or fifth appeal. *That's* when you finally get the services that you deserve. The rates for not being able to keep a job for those with FASD are staggering because their underlying cognitive needs are unrecognized, and they've not enabled success due to the lack of accommodations.

Debbie: Yeah. And it's the same in Ontario.

Bill: Yeah, if people had just an FASD assessment, (it isn't enough here.) They acknowledge the diagnosis but not the disability. (They say that with) a developmental disability, you need to have deficits in at least three of the ten domains. So, they started actually putting that rate in their FASD assessments. This domain, this domain, this domain, and this domain are compromised. Because with just (a diagnosis, without compromised domains), you may have FASD, but nothing (in terms of services.)

Patti: Yes. Well, I think if they covered everybody just on having an FASD diagnosis, they'd go broke in a heartbeat.

Debbie: True enough. Yeah. True enough.

Patti: What else that you guys think would be helpful for folks who self-identify as having an FASD?

Debbie: If you think that you have FASD, pursue it. Because if you've struggled, and if you blamed yourself, and you haven't understood yourself, and people haven't understood you, it (knowing you have FASD) could give you an understanding that you didn't have before. I think for me, too, a lot of times, people come down heavily on parents, moms. And I think if you

162

really understand social stuff, you realize that nobody's doing this on purpose. So that's the first thing I say. Nobody is going out to hurt their children on purpose. So I think teaching people to cut parents some slack because nobody's done this (to their child) on purpose. I often show that little video that Reinier DeSmit developed with his mom, where they talk about FASD, and she talks about using alcohol during pregnancy. (See the Appendix.) They both cry, and he forgives her. I show that (video) a lot because forgiveness is the most important piece. Who wants to go around in the world having a terrible relationship with your parents because of something they didn't mean to do?

Patti: Yeah.

Debbie: And we don't have much time with them.

Patti: Yeah. I have never been angry at my mom over this because, I mean, it was the 60s. Nobody knew better back then.

Debbie: No. Nobody knew any better. And women were starting to become liberated in those years. If you remember, it was back in the 60s that they started going to bars. Remember the bars used to be segregated? So men could take their dates into one area, and (unaccompanied) women could only go into another area. That stuff was starting to change then too, and women were starting to be liberated. My mom was proud. She could drink like a man.

Patti: My brothers remember my mom bragging about drinking my dad under the table (out-drinking my father).

Debbie: Exactly. My mom went out because, you know, if the husband can do it, the woman can do it. Nobody knew better then, so why would I blame her? What she did, she did out of ignorance.

Patti: Well said! Debbie and Bill, this has been delightful! I so very much appreciate your joining me for this conversation.

Epilogue

FASD: The Growing Epidemic

If you resonated with any of the dictated conversations I had within this book, you are not alone. After reading only my story and one of the conversations, my editing team at Amazon Publishing Pros notified me that the team members each recognized people in their lives through what they had read. As I have stated, there are millions of us out there – people who have had no clue that prenatal exposure to alcohol is likely the cause of many of the struggles in their lives.[31] So, now what?

Pursuing a diagnosis as an adult will not magically change anything in life; however, having a framework for understanding the events and struggles in life with this new understanding is priceless, and changes everything. Many of us who came to recognize only in our adult years that we may have been impacted by prenatal exposure to alcohol, have always questioned a lot of things about ourselves: why did we feel like we never fit in, why we weren't good enough, why things easy for so many people were so challenging for us, why we had poor memories, poor impulse control or were forever chasing the shiny new objects in life. Knowing now there are biological reasons for not being able, for example, to process abstract concepts, read body or facial language, recognize danger, or control our impulses brings some peace of mind. If you are fortunate, like a few of us in these pages, to be able to ask your parent if there was drinking during pregnancy, then formal diagnosis is less important than it would be for a youth. If your challenges are more severe, then formal diagnosis can be helpful in getting needed services.

FASD brings with it numerous challenges that none of us in this book would wish upon anyone. However, the reality is that there are millions of people who were affected long before FAS was discovered or the dangers of drinking during pregnancy were known. According to Dr. Ira Chasnoff, FASD is un- or mis-diagnosed 86% of the time.[32] If you, dear reader, have never understood the whys in your life – why you are the way you are, why you have the quirks or struggles that you do – and you resonate with the stories within these pages, then you owe it to yourself to consider: am I one of the 5% of people affected by prenatal exposure to alcohol? Or if, dear reader, you recognize others in your life whom this book appears to describe, then know that the effects are on a spectrum from minimal to severe. While many of us will never live independently, others will function quite well. Take heart! You *can* achieve the things you wish to, with the right workarounds in place. If after reading this book you recognize family or friends within these pages, which is statistically likely, then please recommend this book. Understanding how biology and behavior affect one another – the essence of neurobehavioral conditions – has yielded relief, self-acceptance and self-compassion. Know that those of us within the pages of this book have found these outcomes to be a priceless gift.

Lastly, traditional therapeutic approaches presume that behaviors are intentional choices, and with the right combination of rewards and consequences, the desired behavior change will take place. This is a faulty premise. Neuroscience has *proven* that brain function determines behavior. For this reason, the neurobehavioral model is ideally suited, not only for working with those of us with FASD, but with any brain-based, or neurobehavioral, condition. (I even use this model with my mother, whose dementia has significantly altered her brain function.) I highly recommend working with a Certified Facilitator of the FASCETS Neurobehavioral Model. In doing so, you will not be told, "You could do it if you tried harder," or, "If enough of you wanted life to be better, you would change. You must like being miserable."

Those educated and skilled in understanding neurodivergence – experiencing the world differently – understand that brain function underlies any and all behavior. This model is the foundation of my 120-day *Neurodiversity Mapping Program* for adults. Methodically exploring your unique combination of challenges and strengths is the fast-track for making sense of all the whys, and for creating tailored workarounds to smooth out those areas in life where FASD has been negatively impacting you.

The need is great for professionals to receive training in FASD-informed approaches, whether their discipline is medicine, psychology, psychiatry, addictions recovery, social work, education, law or justice. Remember what I said at the beginning of this book? None of us knew what we didn't know… until we finally learned it. As professionals, we cannot use tools we have never learned. Think of the way we view behavior as a "lens." Until someone gives us new lenses for the glasses through which we view behavior, we will never realize how out of date our "prescription" is. When I think of how I counseled the prospective adoptive families with

165

whom I worked a mere ten years ago, I cringe. FASCETS is a wonderful training organization (full disclosure: I am a Certified Facilitator of the FASCETS Neurobehavioral Model) that offers very affordable training in FASD. This is not the only organization out there; many recommend Families Moving Forward. However Families Moving Forward offers training for a very narrow age range of children. There are others, as well. My four-month *Holistic Parenting Your Neurodivergent Child* program is rooted in FASCETS materials, but adds components I have learned from decades of experience are essential to include in an effective approach.

One reason why there is desperate need for professionals to become competent in FASD-informed care is because without understanding that someone's "behavior" is neurological – reflective of a brain-based disability – they will incorrectly assume the behavior is intentional, and their student/client/patient/suspect will feel blamed, shamed and punished for that which is out of their conscious control. Parents turn to professionals for help, only to be accused of undermining the process, or worse, imagining all their child's behavioral symptoms. If this is the case, needed supports will not be put into place, and outcomes will needlessly worsen. A second reason is because any one professional who *is* FASD-informed can only do so much. Multiplying the number of FASD-informed providers will lead to a sea-change in transforming the way behavior is understood and supported around the world.

Appendix
Resources

First, let me state that this is far from an inclusive list, as the resources are many. For example, I started typing out all the Facebook groups until I realized there were sixty groups! For adults living with FASD, I would suggest Flying with Broken Wings or the supportive community I host, Living with FASD Podcast group. For podcasts, Living with FASD is a podcast I recently launched.

Podcasts:

Living with FASD (my podcast)
FASD Hope, Natalie Vecchione
FASD Family Life, Robbie Seale
Orphans No More, Sandra Flach
The FASD Success Show, Jeff Noble
FASD Informed, NCFASD Informed
Alcohol and Pregnancy, Boston Medical Center
It's a Brain Thing, Oregon Behavior Consultation
Wired Differently, Gilberto Spencer
Spotlight on FASD, Clare Devanney, Glynn and Jessica Rutherford
FASD Elephant, Michael Harris
Girls, Women, Alcohol and Pregnancy
FASD through a Variety of Lenses
NOFASD: Pregnancy and Alcohol, NOFASD

Blogs:

Quirking It, by Rebecca Tillou, www.adultingwithfasd.coms.com
This is What I Know, by CJ Lutke (chapter 2). https://www.nofasd.org.au/community/cj-lutke-blog/
Live Abilities: Create possibilities with hidden differences. Jodeekulp.blogspot.com

CanFASD.ca > has a blog

Support Groups/Zoom Groups:

For Adults:

FASD: Never Alone Support Group. Saturdays/Sundays 12 PM PST. To join via Facebook, contact Miranda Lynne Bezell. To sign up via email, contact Miranda at mandy-gcorp@hotmail.com

Adulting with an FASD (for ages 24+) Group meets the 3rd Monday each month. 4 PM Alaska, 5 PM PST/6 PM MST/7 PM CST/8 PM EST. To register and get zoom invitation, reach out to Proof Alliance. Marissa.hang@proofalliance.org or fasdadultsupport@proofalliance.org

For Parents:

Saturday Support Group. Second Saturday every month, 10-11:30 PST. See Facebook group FASD Network of Southern California.

Aggressive Behaviors Caregiver Support Group Meeting, 4th Thursday evening of the month, 7 PM PST. See Facebook group FASD Network of Southern California.

Websites:

www.patriciakasper.com
ALCFASDChangemakers.com
FASD United.org
FASDNow
https://fafasd.org/wp-content/uploads/2019/02/50fasdfacts_fafasd.pdf
FASCETS.org

emilyhargrovefasdcounselingandconsulting.com

Books:

Trying Differently Rather than Harder, by Diane Malbin

Essential FASD Supports: Understanding and Supporting People with Fetal Alcohol Spectrum Disorders, by Nate Sheets

Blazing New Homeschool Trails: Educating and Launching Teens with Developmental Disabilities, by Natalie Vecchione and Cindy LaJoy

The Silent Epidemic: A Child Psychiatrist's Journey beyond Death Row, Dr. Susan Rich

Tenacity, by Rebecca Tillou

The Accomplice, by Melissa Jacobus

Tiny Titan: A True Story, by Ann Yurcek

A Complicated and Beautiful Brain, by Angela Geddes

It's OK to be You: Living Well with FASD or Other Disabilities, by Kenny LaJoy

Facebook Groups:

As of this writing, Facebook's group search engine identified 60 groups specifically for FASD. Some are geared toward adults with FASD, and some toward caregivers/parents of children with FASD.

I host two Facebook groups. One for adults and one specifically for parents.

Adults: Living with FASD Podcast

Parents: Support for Parents of Kiddos affected by Toxins and Trauma

Pursuing Diagnosis as an Adult:

Paul D. Conner, Ph.D. licensed psychologist and clinical neuropsychologist based in Washington State.

Paul Connor, Ph.D., Clinical Neuropsychologist

22517 7th Ave. South

Des Moines, WA 98198

Ph 206-940-1106

Email: Paul@ConnorNP.com

Liz Redhead Kriston, MS/CCC-SLP, Founder of 121 FASD Services, FASD-informed Speech Language Pathologist

Lizredheadkriston@gmail.com

Ph 828-440-0234

i2ifasd.com

American Academy of Clinical Neuropsychology https://theaacn.org

There is a member directory where you can enter geographical information to narrow your search.

Please note: there was no filter for the search engine for FASD. As with any other profession, FASD is a specialty that requires post-graduate training, and sadly, many practitioners have no clue. When reaching out to a provider from this website, ask for years of experience working specifically with FASD.

Choosing Therapy https://www.choosingtherapy.com/fetal-alcohol-syndrome-adults/

Recovery Village https://www.therecoveryvillage.com/alcohol-abuse/side-effects/fetal-alcohol-syndrome-affects-adulthood/

Please Note: The Recovery Village site (above) lists the very scary outcomes assumed to be prevalent for those affected by FASDs. It is important to note that due to the "youth" of FASD research (only 50 years), the adults in most of these studies were NOT provided effective accommodations and suffered a chronic poor fit between their abilities and the demands of their environment.

It is important to remember that early identification and intervention can prevent these outcomes for today's affected youth.

Videos:

YouTube has an amazing virtual library on FASD, which could occupy hours of someone's time. Below I've listed YouTube videos and channels that are either related to FASD education or to personal experiences living with FASD, three of which are by people featured in Sip by Sip.

FASD: An Introduction, by Gina Schumaker https://youtu.be/Vwj98g8_VTk

Picture This: Life as a Parent of Children with FASD, by Debbie Michaud https://youtu.be/_kjRjcHEG6g

My Adult FASD Diagnosis: Nothing Changed. And Everything Changed. By Reinier DeSmit https://youtu.be/hKaJyKaF1yM

My Adult FASD Diagnosis: Clarity for a Man and his Mom, by Reinier DeSmit https://youtu.be/1oNFd2jDiYA

Module 1 Supporting Students with Fetal Alcohol Spectrum Disorders FASD, by Edmonton Regional Learning Consortium. https://youtu.be/i3753eblUv0 I include this video because of its excellent depiction of how alcohol injures the brain.

Free Friday Tidbits. Youtube.com/@patriciakasperyourfasdcoach Every Friday in 2023, I share a video on another common characteristic of FASD.

References

[1] O'Neil, Erica, The Discovery of Fetal Alcohol Syndrome ((2011-05-09)) Embryo Project Encyclopedia. ISSN: 1940-5030 http://embryo.asu.edu/handle/10776/2100

[2] May PA, Gossage JP. Estimating the prevalence of fetal alcohol syndrome: a summary. Alcohol Res Health2001;25:159-67

[3] Mathers M, Miles K and O'Brian P (2015) Head to Head: Should Women Abstain from Alcohol throughout Pregnancy?, BMJ 2015;351:h5232

[4] National Institute of Alcohol Abuse and Alcoholism, https://www.niaaa.nih.gov Referencing pages on Alcohol Use in the United States and Alcohol Use and Pregnancy in the United States, which were both updated in 2023

[5] Center for Disease Control and Prevention (updated 2023) page on Unintended Pregancy, https://www.cdc.gov/reproductivehealth/contraception/unintendedpregnancy/

[6] Streissguth, A., Fetal Alcohol Syndrome: A Guide for Families and Communities, 1997, pp 96-112)

[7] Malbin, D (Trying Differently rather than Harder

[8] CDC.gov/FASDs/Secondary Conditions

[9] Ibid

[10] Streissguth, AP, Barr HM, Kogan J, et al. Understanding the occurrence of secondary disabilities in clients with Fetal Alcohol Syndrome *FAS) and Fetal Alcohol Effects (FAE). Final report to the CDC, 1996, 96-06.

[11] Supporting Success for Adults with Fetal Alcohol Spectrum Disorders, Feb 2011, Community Living British Columbia, p. 14, 36.

[12] Himmelreich M, Lutke CJ, Hargrove E, The Lay of the Land: Fetal alcohol spectrum disorder (FASD) as a whole body diagnosis, (2020) The Routledge Handbook of Social Work and Addictive Behaviors, edited by Begun A and Murray M, 2020.

[13] Smiley JF et al, Estimates of total neuron number show that neonatal ethanol causes immediate and lasting neuron loss in cortical and subcortical areas, Frontiers in Neuroscience, 02 May 2023, vol 17 2023.

[14] May et al 2018 FASD prevalence > May PA, Chambers CD, Kalberg WO, et al. Prevalence of Fetal Alcohol Spectrum Disorders in 4 US Communities. JAMA. 2018;319(5):474–482. doi:10.1001/jama.2017.21896

[15] Columbia Mailman School of Public Health, Study shows uptick in U.S. alcohol beverage sales during COVID-19 pandemic, August 20, 2021

[16] Author: Daniel DeVise,The Hill, 6/12/23

[17] CanFASDblog/FASD and Adverse Childhood Experiences, 2021

[18] Stigma and FASD, Alcohol and Drug Foundation/FASD, last updated April 28, 2021n
[19] FASD United, blog post, August 2015 https://fasdunited.org/statement-on-fasd-stigma-august-2015/

[20] Amos-Kroohs RM, Fink BA, Smith CJ, Chin L, Van Calcar SC, Wozniak JR, Smith SM. Abnormal Eating Behaviors Are Common in Children with Fetal Alcohol Spectrum Disorder. J Pediatr. 2016 Feb;169:194-200.e1. doi: 10.1016/j.jpeds.2015.10.049. Epub 2015 Nov

[21] Ibid

[22] What is FASD, Proof Alliance, www.proofalliance.org/what-is-fasd/living-with-fasd/.

[23] Ibid

[24] Op cit, Community Living British Columbia, p. 11

[25] Ibid, p. 11

[26] Ibid, p. 36.

[27] Difficulty with Abstract & Conceptual Thinking, Duke University, Understanding Fetal Alcohol Spectrum Disorders (FASD): a comprehensive guide for pre-K – 8 educators, chapter 5

[28] Stevens, S., Dudek, J., Nash, K., Koren, G., & Rovet, J. (2015). Social Perspective Taking and Empathy in Children with Fetal Alcohol Spectrum Disorders. Journal of the International Neuropsychological Society, 21(1), 74-84. doi:10.1017/S1355617714001088

[29] Ory N, Why some people can "say" or "talk" more than they can understand and remember, 2004, challengingbehavior@shaw.ca

[30] Tasse M, The relation between intellectual functioning and adaptive behavior in the diagnosis of intellectual disability, AAIDD (American Association on Intellectual and Developmental Disabilities), Dec 1, 2016 https://doi.org/10.1352/1934-9556-54.6.381

173

[31]"...we should be very humbled by the 99.99% of people with FASD who are undiagnosed." (Svetlana Popova, Danijela Dozet, and Larry Burd, "Fetal Alcohol Spectrum Disorder: Can We Change the Future?" Alcoholism: Clinical and Experimental Research 44, no. 4 [2020]: 815-819, https://doi.org/10.1111/acer.14317).

[32]   Dr.   Chasnoff   prevalence   of   missed/mis-dx:
https://pediatrics.aappublications.org/content/early/2015/01/07/peds.2014-2171

Made in United States
North Haven, CT
29 January 2024

48081221R00108